Lee Hazlewood's
The Pope's
Daughter

93-HAZL

Lee Hazlewood's
The Pope's
Daughter

His Fantasy Life with

Nancy and Other Sinatra's

Lee Hazlewood

To order additional copies of this book, contact:
Xlibris Corporation
1-888-7-XLIBRIS
www.Xlibris.com
Orders@Xlibris.com

Contents

A FORWARD DOESN'T NECESSARILY MEAN
ANYTHING 9
WILL THE LAST ONE TO LEAVE
THE 'GARDEN OF EDEN',
PLEASE IMPEDE THE SNAKE 13
FOR EVERY SOLUTION, THERE IS A PROBLEM 18
COMPLACENCY IS THE
MOTHER OF SUCCESS 22
THOSE WHO BREACH COMMANDANT #7,
OFTEN INVEST HEAVILY
IN ZIPPER STOCK 27
NEVER TRUST A SACRIFICIAL
LAMB RIDING A UNICYCLE 33
THE BIG SPIRIT GIVETH AND
THE BIG SPIRIT TAKETH AWAY
(NOT A BAD DEAL – BETTER THAN
YOU'LL GET FROM THE
TAX COLLECTOR) 38
TWO FISH WILL FEED FIVE THOUSAND,
IF 4,998 ARE NOT HUNGRY 41
HE THAT SITETH ON A HOT STOVE
– SHALL RISE AGAIN 44
THANKS GUYS. . . . . . .
I'LL TAKE IT FROM HERE . . .L.H. 48
THE FIRST OF
MANY SUMMIT MEETINGS 53
THIS BOOT IS MADE FOR WALKING 57

THE DAY BEFORE "D"-DAY *64*

EUROPE ON $$$$$$ A DAY *68*

ROME *70*

PARIS *73*

HAMBURG *76*

LONDON *78*

THE HOMECOMING *82*

MAMA *86*

A FEW MORE RECORDS
  AND SOME AVERAGES *89*

HA HA HA GETS DRAFTED *94*

SISTER, BROTHER, DADDY *97*

THE RETURN OF HA HA HA *104*

JEANETTE MCDONALD
  IN BOOTS –
  NELSON EDDY IN JEANS *108*

THREE WEEKS LATER 109

LONDON BRIDGE IS FALLING *111*

WE WENT TO NASHVILLE TO RECORD 'JACKSON' OR
  WAS IT THE OTHER WAY *114*

MOVIN' WITH
  WHAT'S HER "HA" *120*

THE MEEK SHALL INHERIT ADROITNESS *125*

A FORWARD DOESN'T NECESSARILY MEAN ANYTHING

SO LET'S HAVE ONE

WHAT'S IT LIKE TO WORK WITH A NANCY SINATRA? They ask it, and ask it, and when you have answered, they ask it again. And the 'ahs' and 'ers' come pouring from your mouth like so many miles of frozen string melting from each desperate tug of a left hand filled with warm adjectives. And because you will not free your sinful right hand (so happily engaged in mental masturbation), and swim for shore, you drown in a sea of sometimes kind, seldom clever, never interesting and mostly biased anecdotes.

So perhaps in our little story it is best we stay with feelings, failings and fantasies, shying away from graffitied walls of truth where someone has bothered to engrave it all, just as it happened, but didn't!

What's it like to work with a Nancy Sinatra? It's a visit to Disneyland, only your father owns all the rides. It's an evening in the medicine cabinet of Edgar Allen Poe's mother. It's a trip on Superman's cape and you are too frightened to look down for fear you'll discover your real identity. It's a Sousa march and the

phallic cymbals are playing melody. It's a plastic palace where all that glitters is gold. It's a Las Vegas stage,
sitting on a two-dollar stool in front of a fifty-two-piece
orchestra, next to a lady in a five thousand-dollar
gown; you're singing a little flat and wondering if
the fly is open on your eight-dollar 'jeans'. It's Beauty
and the Beast selling a 'fix' to the Mickey Mouse
People. It's frustrating, foolish, Falstaffian, freaky,
fucked-up and fun.

So let us begin at the beginning. . . . . . .

WILL THE LAST ONE TO LEAVE THE 'GARDEN OF EDEN', PLEASE IMPEDE THE SNAKE

IN THE BEGINNING (now, I'm talking about the beginning of the beginning) there was NOTHING! NOTHING! NOTHING, but the BIG SPIRIT. That's not exactly true – 'cause the BIG SPIRIT (B.S.) had a "little inner voice" (l.i.v.) and <u>that</u> was all there was. . . . .

B.S. and l.i.v. and baskets and baskets of NOTHING!

B.S. spoketh to l.i.v. (who else?) and sayeth, "I <u>feel</u>eth creative. I have not <u>felt</u>eth creative before, but I <u>feel</u>eth creative <u>now</u>eth!"

"So?" queried l.i.v.

"I shall <u>create</u>eth '<u>up</u>eth and <u>down</u>eth'"

"Hmm, <u>up</u>eth and <u>down</u>eth? Needs something." Observed l.i.v.

""What would you <u>suggest</u>eth?"

"How about Heaven and Earth?"

"You <u>think</u>eth so?"

"Yeah. . . ."

"Oketh, here it cometh" expounded B.S.

BIG BANG!!!

"Wow!"

"You liketh?"

"You give great 'creative", B.S.!"

"Thanketh you."

"What's next?"

"At times I know noteth . . . at other times I knoweth . . . then . . ."

"Could we move on?"

"Oh, sorry . . . how about darketh and not-darketh," voicedeth the BIG SPIRIT.

l.i.v. thought just an eon and slovenly burped, "If that's what you want to do next, you've got about as much dark as your ever gonna need. Why not 50% dark and 50% light?"

"What's light?" wondereth aloud B.S.

"Light is 'not-dark'," grunted l.i.v.

"Oh, I caneth do that . . . here it cometh!"

BIG BANG!!!

"Good stuff! B.S.

" . . . and I'll call 'darketh' . . . NIGHT! . . . and I'll call 'not-darketh' . . . 'NOT NIGHT!!

" . . . And you're about to make a mess of the whole

thing!" l.i.v. spake. "Night is good, but why don't you keep things simple and call 'not-dark' . . . DAY?"

"You <u>think</u>eth so?"

"I know so."

"Then it shall <u>bee</u>th, now . . . I'll make big bunches of wet and call it . . . uh.."

"Ocean or sea sounds good."

"Yes, it <u>doese</u>th! . . . Then I'll <u>create</u>th stupendous bunches of 'UGH' and divide the oceans . . . and . . ."

"Hold it . . . Hang on . . . What's 'UGH'?"

"'UGH' is the firmament that divides the. . . ."

"Oh . . . OK . . . Do you like the sound of LAND?"

"Yes! Yes! Oceans and land." <u>Howled</u>eth the BIG SPIRIT.

"But I thought you already created the land and Earth?"

"Hmm . . . perhaps I <u>did</u>eth, but who's to know? Here it <u>come</u>th!!!"

<u>BIG BANG!!!</u>

Breathless and <u>consumed</u>eth with power, the BIG SPIRIT <u>screamed</u>eth "And now I shall cover the Earth in green . . . uh . . ."

"Grass?"

"Yes, grass! And I shall <u>make</u>th tall things with sweet things hanging . . ."

"Trees and fruit!?"

"Yes, and I shall <u>make</u>th four seasons." <u>sangeth</u> B.S.

"How many is <u>four</u> BIG SPIRIT?"

"Four is one more than three and one less than five. . . . . pay attention!!"

"You got it, Big Fella!!!!"

" . . . And the seasons shall be <u>called</u>eth..<u>Spring</u>eth, <u>Summer</u>eth, <u>Fall</u>eth, and Winter!"

" . . . Cool!"

"Correct! Winter shall be very cool! . . . And I shall <u>create</u>th all the 'blinkies' in the heavens!"

"Wait a bit . . . Blinkies?"

"Do you <u>prefer</u>eth 'boobies'? . . . I sorta like . . . "

"No . . . no . . . how about . . . <u>stars</u>? . . . Sounds less childlike." Hummed little inner voice.

"I like <u>stars</u>! Whats childlike?"

"I have no idea, B.S."

"It matters not! . . . And I'll <u>create</u>th a big ball of fire to light the day and something else to light the night . . . well?"

"Sorry, B.S., I'm fresh out of ideas for naming two big balls."

"No sweat, little inner voice. It's of small importance. Ready! Get a grip on your 'quang' this should be a <u>LuLu</u>!!!" bellowedeth B.S.

"B.S. . . . What's a LULU?"

"Don't bother me now . . . I'm making it <u>cometh</u> . . . oh . . . oh . . . oh"

<u>BIG BANG</u>!!!

And the Angels sang:
I have walked these streets a thousand times
And never seen another face
I have loved a hundred, hell two hundred
And I never left a trace
You were just another place to stop
As good as any place to be
Then your thunder and your lightning
God your thunder and you lightning
Got to me

Song: "Your Thunder And Your Lightning" Lee Hazlewood ©

FOR EVERY SOLUTION, THERE IS A PROBLEM

"I GOT IT!"

"You <u>go</u>teth what?"

"A name for the two balls" smirked little inner voice "the day ball will be called the 'sun' and the night ball, the moon."

"You <u>think</u>eth these good names?"

Well, we could call the day ball 'piss' and the night ball 'shit' – but we might find better use for those words later."

"Perhaps you're <u>right</u>eth . . . the sun and the moon!" The *BIG SPIRIT lowered his head in deep contemplation. "Today shall be my almost nearly, but not quite hardly creative day . I will <u>create</u>th all the creatures of the sky that fly and all the creatures in the sea that swim and <u>most</u> of the creatures that roam the earth from the cattle to the '<u>creep</u>eth crawlies' . . ."*

"Whoa! . . . What are 'creepy crawlies'?"

"Reptiles that are so small they lie at your feet and <u>make</u>th pleasant sounds."

"B.S. you think there's any chance these creepy crawlies might grow big?"

"Perhaps, little inner voice, but I have made them kind, so feareth not."

BIG BANG!!!

"You got a name for those hairy animals that sometimes stand up and walk?"

"Yes, they are apes. The small one are monkeys, the next ones are chimps, and the largest are gorillas."

"Apes, huh? Are they kind?"

"Would I have madeth them . . . if they were noteth?"

"The large ones are called gorillas, huh?"

"Correcteth little inner voice"

"I just saw a gorilla hit a tree . . . a very tall, big tree . . . the tree screamed and fell over dead."

"Can this be trueth, l.i.v.?"

"It can be and is . . . and that isn't all."

"There's moreth?"

"A lot more. Then the gorilla ate the tree and everything in or on it . . ."

B.S. was heard to sayeth "It would seem not all my creations are perfect."

"I wouldn't worry about it B.S. There's not many gorillas, but there are more of those creepy crawlies than you can count and most of 'em grew taller than two trees. They're eating everything in sight including each other. And they crap so much they're making

mountains of crap!! At the rate they're going, it won't be long before they tilt the earth."

"What you _telleth_ me _paineth_ me so. What _thinketh_ you I should do?"

"Waste 'em!!"

"_Destroyeth_ one of my creations!"

"You got that right!! And soon, but . . . not too soon."

"Why _shouldeth_ I wait?"

"'Cause when one of 'em dies they turn into some strange 'black gooey stuff'. Most of 'em are in the Middle East now, and if you liquidate them you're gonna make an ocean of 'black gooey stuff'!! So maybe you should wait 'till some leave the Middle East."

The BIG SPIRIT's face lined with pain as he _contemplateth_ what must be done. "Those BIG creepy crawlies, they are a _mistaketh_, they must _goeth_! But worry _noteth_ I shall cover the ocean of strange 'black gooey stuff' with sand. Much sand."

"OK, B.S. It's your decision. Say . . . while you're in a destructive mood, could you get rid of mosquitoes too?"

BIG BANG!!!

And the Angels sang:
    I heard my brother died last week
    Or was it just a rumor
    From an overdose of hate
    Taken in his veins
    I heard God must have a sense of humor

'Cause when they put him in his grave
It didn't even rain
It's a cold, hard world love
And these are cold, hard times
It's a cold, hard world love
And these are cold, hard times

Song: "Cold Hard Times" – Lee Hazlewood ©

COMPLACENCY IS THE MOTHER OF SUCCESS

"*TELLETH ME little inner voice, how long do you estimateth I've been creating?*"

"*This is the sixth day.*"

"*Seems liketh millions of years.*"

"*It probably is B.S., depends on whose system you're using. And what are you doing 'OLD GREAT ONE', playing in the dirt?*"

A smile of tired madness raced across the face of the **BIG SPIRIT** *and he replied* "*I will on this dayeth createth* **MAN!**"

"*Swell, what is a man?*"

"*It is my likeness. He will looketh like me. He will beeth my mirror. He will . . .*"

"*Have you been smoking some of the green leaf? Mirrors break! And you know what that means . . . seven years of bad . . .*"

"*Hush!!*"

"You got it 'omnipotent codger'. However, you look a little fatigued. Perhaps you should rest."

"I shall resteth on the seventh day"

"A little holiday, then you create MAN . . . sounds like a plan to me B.S. You don't do your best work when you're debilitated, remember the gooey creepy crawlies??"

Sadness dripped from the platitudinous eyes of the BIG SPIRIT as he countered, "One little mistake. You'll never let me forgeteth!"

"I hate redundancy, but, there's a few more. What about the mosquitoes . . .

"ON THIS SIXTH DAY, I SHALL CREATETH MAN!"

"Shouldn't you wait 'til you've rested, B.S.?"

"NO!!"

"Right you are! Old Heavenly Bully!!"

"MAN shall have a head, arms, legs, and shall walketh upright."

"Sounds like a gorilla to me."

"Correcteth, but with less hair."

"So man will be a less-haired gorilla?"

"Yes, but there's moreth. He willeth have a large brain and will thinketh for himself and control his own destiny."

"You've been walking in the poppy fields again, haven't you B.S.?"

"He willeth have a voice and be able to speaketh, just as you and I."

"Oh My God!" screeched l.i.v.

"Yes?"

"It's just a cliché . . . forget it, B.S."

"And he will be able to singeth."

"Man's gonna sing? I thought you gave Angels the singing franchise."

"*They will <u>understand</u>eth.*"

"*One of the three or four things the Angels do and you give one of 'em to MAN. You better check with your Angels buddy, some of those Angels are BAD!!*"

"*It <u>matter</u>eth not. It shall <u>beeth</u>! And man shall have a small pure white spot in his <u>head</u>eth and this shall be his connection to me. It shall be <u>named</u>eth his SOUL. What <u>think</u>eth you little inner voice?*"

"*Let me get this straight. Man's gonna control his own destiny.*"

"*Yes.*"

"*And you're giving him a large brain and a small soul.*"

"*Yes. This <u>trouble</u>th you?*"

"*Oh, hell yes. Why not a small brain and a large soul?*"

"*No, I shall <u>trust</u>eth man . . . my greatest creation.*"

"*Don't carve that in stone B.S., unless you have a big eraser.*"

"*Now follow me and <u>feast</u>eth your eyes on my master-piece – MAN. Why <u>mull</u>eth you?*"

"*I see you've made several.*"

"*Yes.*"

"*The smaller ones are kinda cute, B.S.".*"

"*Yes, those <u>are</u>th women . . . man's mates. They will <u>multiply</u>eth and soon there will be millions.*"

"*B.S., when they do this mating and multiplying, are they going about it in the same fashion as the apes?*"

"*<u>Almost</u>eth the same.*"

"*Boy, B.S., that mating is an ugly thing to see. They wiggle around, moan and groan and make lots of noise just before they stop. It's one nasty mess.*"

"*I am <u>open</u>eth to suggestions!*"

"*Well, why don't you just have 'em shake hands . . .*

and another thing, why did you create so many flavors of man?"

"Their many colors shall <u>maketh</u> a beautiful bouquet to <u>glorifyeth</u> the earth and me."

"Yeah, but what if the purple ones don't like the green ones?"

"This <u>caneth</u> never happen."

"You wanna bet!!!"

And the Angels sang:
Cowards and Heroes
Listen my friends
If you have money
Or nothing to spend
It'll make no difference
In a hundred years or so
Sooner or later
We all make the little flowers grow

Wise men and fools
Two'll get you five
You'll never get
Out of this world alive
Don't run and hide
It's no use I know
Sooner or later
We all make the little flowers grow

Short men and tall men
And all the rest
Please don't blame me
I didn't start this mess
Some of us stay
Some of us go

Sooner or later
We all make the little flowers grow

Song: *"We All Make The Little Flowers Grow" – Lee
Hazlewood* ©

THOSE WHO BREACH COMMANDANT #7, OFTEN INVEST HEAVILY IN ZIPPER STOCK

" . . . *AND WHAT DO you* <u>thinketh</u> *on little inner voice?"*

"The truth is 'Old Holy Bubba', I was thinking about MAN. I was thinking . . . giving them a large brain and complete control of their destinies was a brave and good thing . . ."

"<u>Reallyeth</u>?"

" . . . *This is until you got displeased, sometime back, and decided to drown 'em all . . . with the exception of that weird, boat maker and his family."*

Silence.

"That was your idea . . . wasn't it?"

Silence.

"No matter . . . Then the Big 'M' comes down off the mountain with stone tablets and he tells the folks YOU

*wrote 10 rules and restrictions that they must live by . . .
after all this time. Did you come up with these rules?"*

Silence.

*"Well, most of 'em are good . . . you shouldn't kill
and you shouldn't steal, etc. However, people really, really like to mate and not just to reproduce, but for <u>GIT
DOWN</u>, <u>GOOD-FEELIN' FUN!</u>"*

*"And you've slapped 'em with a rule to make 'em feel
despicably guilty and takes all the joy out of it."*

*"Did you give the Big 'M' that no mating rule that
says you should only mate with one person for your entire
life??"*

Silence.

*"Not very talkative today are we? Anyway, that's not
a popular rule.*

*Have you ever considered exchanging it for 'Thou
shalt kill at least 30 mosquitoes each day?*

Silence.

*"And now here's the 'Biggie'!! Some people think you
had a son that walked this earth. Some others believe
he's still on the way. Then there's people who don't believe any of it."*

"Did you have a son?"

"I've <u>hadeth</u> many sons."

"Swell, for awhile I thought you had laryngitis!"

*"Most all the men and women believe in you. Which
is just 'duckie'! But they all worship you in different ways
and they get angry (we're talking real wrathful here) if
somebody doesn't believe the way they do.*

You know all this, huh?"

"<u>Harrumpheth</u>!!"

*"Oh, boy, I spend most of the day talking to you and
I get four apathetic chunks of silence and one lethargic
'harrumph!"*

"Do you realize how many people on earth have writ-

ten books about you and your conversations with them? And now they have telegraph, telephones, automobiles.. and __RADIO__!!. All these folks on the radio screaming to send them money 'cause they know you personally. Just mention your name, the money comes and the money-senders problems are solved."

"There's this lady on the radio begging for money so she can buy brassieres, for cows, so their teets won't be exposed and jockstraps, for donkeys, so you won't see their dicks!!"

"There's some crazies down there! Have you considered turning on the 'blessed faucet' again, 'OLD Preeminent, Invincible, Supreme One'?"

"__Harrumpheth! Harrumpheth__!!"

"Fantastic! I got a double __harrumpheth__!!"

"Shit, I remember when men and women ran around 'the garden' wearing nothing. They were beautiful! No shame, no guilt. They were so naked, you could see their thoughts."

"You __troubleth__ me, l.i.v."

"Geez, I'm sorry B.S. How do I trouble you?"

"I __feeleth__ you have only loathing for MAN . . . my greatest creation."

"May I fall and land face-down in a pool of 'holy hairlips', if I'm fabricating, 'cause I love the insignificant little dipshits!!"

"You __doeth__?"

"I do!! They war, they lie, they pillage, they don't keep your rules. But, B.S., their music embarrasses the Angels. Have you listened to Bach or Beethoven? They sing. Have you heard Caruso or the 'railroad man' Jimmy Rogers? They paint. Have you seen the Mona Lisa or the roof of the Sistene Chapel or the simple beauty of Grandma Moses paintings. . . ??"

"__Enougheth! Enougheth__! You do __loveth__ them."

"You got that right, B.S."

"Then I <u>haveth</u> a small task for you."

"I don't believe I've ever performed a task for you, 'O' Heavenly Lollipop'"

"You <u>shouldeth</u> take yourself to the L.O.L.C. area and get as <u>mucheth</u> information as possible on this number . . . 209976620-06228-8414" and then the Big Spirit was gone leaving l.i.v. to ponder . . .

1. *Why do white chickens lay brown eggs?*
2. *Why is satyriasis so misunderstood?*
3. *Why don't American Indians trust the US Government?*
4. *Why does a handicapped male dog, with two front legs and one back leg, have problems urinating?*
5. *Why can most birds whistle through their peckers?*
6. *WHERE THE HELL IS THE L.O.L.C. AREA and WHAT DOES IT MEAN?*

l.i.v. wandered the cosmos, hungering for some small clue to the whereabouts of the L.O.L.C. area. He asked 'little-chicken-little' who replied, "The sky is falling!! The sky is falling!!"

"Hey, you feathered, little-clucker, I know the guy that made the sky. It's made good! It ain't falling!!!

"It isn't?" peeped 'little-chicken-little'.

"No, it isn't!!"

'Little-chicken-little' thought a moment, then walked away shouting "The sky isn't falling! The sky <u>is</u> <u>not</u> falling!!"

Two Angels, dressed in black with white blindfolds and being lead by a group of rather large 'seeing-eye mosquitoes', were next to cross the path of l.i.v . . . l.i.v. thought. Could this be why HE made those damn mosquitoes!

"*You know where the L.O.L.C. area is? L.i.v. asked.*

"*How could we know? We can't see.*"

"*Take off those silly blindfolds and you can!!*"

The Angels slowly removed the blindfolds and as their eyes became adjusted to the light, one sang. "Oh! That's so much better."

"*Whats with the blindfolds?" l.i.v. inquired.*

"*We are training the mosquitoes, so they can lead useful lives.*"

"*Waste the useless bastards!! They're a mistake!*" *grunted l.i.v., walking away.*

l.i.v. wandered and wandered and wandered some more, then he spotted a green troll, sitting on a pink stool, under a sign.

"L.O.L.C. AREA"
Lives of Little Consequence

"*What do you want??" griped the troll.*

"*I need some information.*"

"*Do I look like I know anything?*"

"*You look like a green troll, sitting on a pink stool, under a sign that reads: L.O.L.C., who's about to participate in an ass-kickin' contest with me – and you know whose ass I'm gonna use!!*"

The troll dropped his head and whispered "Then, how can I help you?"

"*Here." L.i.v. spoke 'Give me all the information you have on this number . . . 20997620-06228-8414.*"

The troll looked at the number, pushed a small button on the underside of his pink stool and from nowhere came the report which he handed to l.i.v.

"*There! Now are you happy?*"

"*I'll be happy – when you get nice!!!*"

"But, I'm a green troll, nowhere does it say, I'm sup-posed to be nice!"

"Then you better get nice!" warned l.i.v. "Or I'll come back here and cut off something you really need and make you live under a bridge!"

And the Angels sang:
Friday's child
Born a little ugly
Friday's child
Good looks passed him by
Friday's child
Makes something look like nothing
Friday's child am I

Song: "Friday's Child" – Lee Hazlewood ©

NEVER TRUST A SACRIFICIAL LAMB RIDING A UNICYCLE

MEMO: From the BIG SPIRIT
To: little inner voice
1957

Concerning the L.O.L.C. Area

This is an experiment:
Almost no one, from the L.O.L.C. Area, has accomplished anything of any note (by earthly standards). However, I believe you, l.i.v., might be able to correct this, by placing yourself in the dreams of this subject and making suggestions. However, use great caution for he might think you an incubus.

He will not have any recollection of your suggestions when he is awake.

But perhaps, some of your ideas will seep into his conscious thoughts and help him overcome his life of little consequence.

It's worth a try – I Hope!

The Subject: Barton Lee Hazlewood

Born: Mannford, Oklahoma (Pop. 356) 1929

His father, Gabe, is a wildcatter (one who drills in the earth for the gooey 'creepy crawlies' remains (now called oil). He was very successful in this business until 1937 when he went broke, but continued to work in the same profession, for others, until he went to work on government construction projects during WWII. He is at this time (1957) gainfully employed doing the same.

His mother, Evalee Robinson-Hazlewood, is a small,

80lb,sanity challenged, hyper, extremely verbal woman. Great cook, great pastry maker, great seamstress (show her a photo and she'll make it). She is never contented, when the 'statis' stays 'quo', and often explodes in a one woman chorus of words that would embarrass a seasoned sailor. She loves her son more than she loves ME.

Barton Lee Hazlewood is almost 28 years. His childhood was less than noticeable until his third birthday. His father gave him a german shepard puppy, whose favorite sport was biting his young master, Barton Lee's favorite sport was biting the dog back and depositing him in the refrigerator. Their strange friendship lasted until Barton Lee locked him in the deep freeze one August day and went out to play.

He started to stutter when he was 5 years old (Lee – not the dog) and did not stop until the summer of his seventh year (he will not laugh or tell jokes to this day concerning people with speech impediments).

Gabe's work took his family to many southwest cities and Lee attended 5 schools in the eighth grade. His father promised him they would live in <u>one</u> place until Lee completed high school. They settled in Groves, Texas and Lee went to, and graduated, from high school at Port Neches-Groves, Texas. His high school marks were all A's & B's, not because Lee was such a good scholar, but Gabe had rules, "make a 'C' or lower and you stay home 9 weeks until next report card". Lee liked his social life more than he minded studying-consequently no 'C's'.

Lee went to college, married, went to Korea for 18 months, went back to college and got a job making $55.00 a week as a disc jockey in Coolidge, Arizona. Fathered Debra & Mark (whom he loves more than he does ME). Got fired, moved to Phoenix where he is now working as a DJ for $105.00 per week.

So l.i.v., my old friend, see what you can do to change the life of this unremarkable person. Remember, it's an experiment. Try to do better with this assignment than I did with the 'creepy crawlies'.

THE BIG SPIRIT
Typed by Angel #17-2156
(who refused to type any
word ending with 'eth')

And the Angels sang:

I was born in Mannford Oklahoma
I was born in Mannford town
When you're born
In Mannford Oklahoma
There ain't no 'up'
In your cup
There's just 'down'

Song: Mannford Oklahoma – Lee Hazlewood ©

THE BIG SPIRIT GIVETH AND THE BIG SPIRIT TAKETH AWAY (NOT A BAD DEAL – BETTER THAN YOU'LL GET FROM THE TAX COLLECTOR)

"Oh, Marilyn . . . right there, Marilyn . . . oh, that's it . . . don't stop . . ."

"Excuse me . . . are you Barton Lee Hazlewood?'

"Excuse you!! . . . You're screwing with my screwing . . . Now get the fuck out of my dream . . . Look what you've done!! . . . Bye, Marilyn, see you soon.."

"Bye . . . Bye . . . Bye" whispered Marilyn and she evaporated.

"Whataya doing in my dream, 'shit for brains'?"

l.i.v. smiled and moved closer "When you dream," he asked, "you <u>actually</u> know you're dreaming?"

Lee shook the sleep clouds from his subconscious and asked "little space putz . . . did you ever dream you were awake and wake up asleep?"

"I don't undertand your meaning" pondered l.i.v.

"It figures!"

"So you <u>do</u> <u>know</u> when you're dreaming?"

"Yessss!"

"Might I ask how you know?"

"I know' little glob of weirdness' because I feel fantastic when I'm dreaming and I don't always feel good when I'm awake. Now . . ."

"Do you remember your <u>dreams</u> when you are awake?"

"No . . . never have . . . probably never will!"

"Good!" l.i.v. whispered, then said "I'm here to help you, if that's possible!"

"Where are you from 'little space-o' and why the fuck would you want to help ME? Are you one of those little freaks from Roswell, New Mexico? Listen!! I don't believe in any of that U.F.O. and spaceman shit. Hell, I don't even believe in New Mexico. If someone wanted to give an enema to America, they'd stick the hose in New Mexico. It's the worst of all the states. If it were mine, I'd pave the son-of-a-bitch from one end to the other.!!!."

"I wouldn't know, I've never been there" l.i.v. explained.

"The hell you say!! Well never mind. Whataya want, space-o?"

"As I said before, I've come to help you. I have read scriptures stating ' last year you wrote and produced a hit record'."

"Yeah! 'The Fool' – Sanford Clark."

"I assume you made considerable monies for this?"

"Hell no, time I paid off my debts, put a new top on my '49 Pontiac convertible, and paid the I.R.S. . . . ."

"The I.R.S.???

"Government, <u>taxes</u>, space-o!! <u>Taxes</u>!!! I didn't have 15 dollars left."

"So you are surviving on $105 a week?"

"Listen, you 'Flash Gordon roadie', I gotta pay taxes on that too, so I get about $82 a week."

"And?"

"I'd file for bankruptcy, but it's too expensive!"

"Are you planning any new productions?" questioned
l.i.v.

*"Look, you inquisitive 'worm sperm', I don't have any
idea what I'm gonna do next."*

*"What about that young man, you like, who plays gui-
tar?"* asked *l.i.v.*

*"Duane Eddy? Well, I like the guy and he picks good
guitar, but . . . wait a minute . . . see ya . . . I'm waking up
. . ."*

And the Angels sang:

> *My old barn's about to cave in*
> *It'll fall right on the house I'm in*
> *My burial insurance is overdue again*
> *Still I might break even this year*
>
> *Well, the taxman says he don't mean me no harm*
> *But if I don't pay, they're gonna take my farm*
> *If they do that, just as sure as you're born*
> *I might break even this year*
>
> *A republican's vote's 50 cents and a wink*
> *A democrat's vote's a dollar and a drink*
> *If I vote for 'em both, I'll do better I think*
> *And I might break even this year*

Song: *"I Might Break Even This Year"* – Lee Hazlewood ©

TWO FISH WILL FEED FIVE THOUSAND, IF 4,998 ARE NOT HUNGRY

Little by little . . . a little bit later.

"Soeth??? L.i.v. speaketh to me about Lee."

"Well, old 'starmaker'. He's a very strange human . . . not that they all aren't strange . . . he's past strange . . . spend a little time with him and weird seems normal.""

"Explaineth yourself l.i.v."

"It's his talent that I question. His complete music studies are a three year stint playing snare drum, with the Port Neches-Groves High School Texas marching Band. That's it! He's no List or Wagner, but somehow he manages to write songs on this guitar he got somewhere . . . and he learned chords watching musicians at recording sessions he produces.

The man makes no secret of his Lilliputian talent. However, his dwarfish gifts, for songwriting and record *producing, earn him gargantuan sums of $$ . . . something he loves."*

"So he <u>lov</u>eth money."

"Correct!! Old 'moon designer', he loves his children, money, fast cars, gambling, liberal politicians, barely legal women and YOU. But I would dare not suggest the 'order'."

"Has he <u>found</u>eth happiness?"

"He should have, but it's difficult to know . . . he's secretive . . . mostly about money. His good friend and favorite studio guitarist, Al Casey, upon seeing a huge sign, covering the side of a mountain, between Phoenix and Los Angeles (praising one of your sons), that read, "JESUS SAVES!!!" Casey was heard to respond, "YES, BUT NOT LIKE LEE HAZLEWOOD!!!"

"He's sold millions of albums (before CD's) and singles on his guitar picking buddy, Duane Eddy, with titles like 'Rebel Rouser', "40 Miles Of Bad Road', 'Because They're Young', 'Dance With The Guitar Man', etc. But Duane and Lee feel the record company has more 'sets of books' than an Oklahoma bootlegger!"

"They <u>are</u>th being cheated??"

"Your conservative observations challenge the creation of mosquitoes, 'old darling deity'."

And the Angels hummed:
  Dah-a-dong
  Dong dong dong dong
  Dah-a-dong
  Dong dong dong dong
  Dah-a-dong
  Dong dong dong dong
  Dong dong dong dong dong
  Dah-a-dong

Song: "Rebel Rouser" – Duane Eddy and Lee Hazlewood © (instrumental)

HE THAT <u>SIT</u>ETH ON A HOT STOVE – SHALL RISE AGAIN

"Oh, Marilyn . . . it's so good . . . so very good . . ."

"Oh, Lee, it's wonderful . . . may I ask you something?" whined Marilyn.

"Certainly, my love."

"When it really gets good . . ."

"Yes?"

"Really, really, really, good . . ."

"Yes?"

"Why do you always scream <u>your</u> name?"

"I lead a life of noisy desperation, my 'blonde Persephone'."

"Good morning, my friends." Grunted l.i.v. "I see you're still dancing the 'Mating Dance of Dances'!"

"Goodbye, sweet love." Whispered Marilyn (wondering to herself – 'when it's good, really, really good, perhaps I should scream out my name sometimes') and she was gone.

"You've done it again, you no-dick space-o, stay out of my dreams!!!"

"Oh, madcap, mediocre, madrigal maker from Mannford, we have much to speak of!" cried l.i.v., having little, if any, fear of ending his sentence with a preposition. "We have no-thing to speak about . . . NOTHING!"

"I see you have furloughed your sprightly self from Phoenix and purchased a mammoth Spanish house in Toluca Lake, California, with a pool as sweeping as the Mediterranean . . . You must be very successful."

"I have no money. I'm broke."

"I place little credence in your words." chimed l.i.v. "Your songs and records with Duane Eddy have sold millions. You must be . . ."

"Can't you hear, 'planet breath', I am broke, penurious, without funds, impoverished, on my ASS!!"

"How is it your children attend private schools? You can afford the company of beautiful women . . . who depend on your kindness . . . stranger!" (I really loved "A Streetcar Named Desire" thought l.i.v.) " . . . 2 Jaguars, a 'Caddy' . . . contributions to liberal politicians and charities only you know or understand . . ." l.i.v. moped

" . . . Well. . . ?"

"All that stuff mystifies you, doesn't it! It really mystifies me, too, NUMB-NUTS!!"

"Am I to understand, Warner Brothers wants you to produce the youth group 'Dino, Desi, & Billy'?"

"Yes. But I ain't. Dino is Dean Martin's son (13 years), Desi is Lucy Ball and Desi Arnaz's son (12 years) and Billy's father owns ½ of Beverly Hills. Although I need the money . . . THEY DON'T . . . so . . . now go! . . . 8am . . . I'm waking up. . . . . . ."

Meanwhile back in Nirvana

"You looketh troubled, little inner voice." Spaketh the 'Mighty of Mighties'.

"Well, 'Old Jehovah Jones' I am. You gave me a small task, a simple task, a lucid task, but I'm like a holy broken abacus, you can't count on me!! My efforts have proved ineffective."

"Tsk, tsk, tsketh, your subconscious suggestions, in HIS dreams, have hadeth a most positive effect on one Barton Lee Hazlewood #209976620-06228-8414, for it is knowneth throughout the land, this less than average being, has excelled and madeth outstanding profits in the record business!"

"I've made you happy?" warbled l.i.v.

B.S. smiled 'Yes' and the heavens shook and so did parts of Winnie, Texas.

l.i.v continued "Well . . . he did produce 3 albums (before CD's) and 4 singles for 'Dino, Desi, & Billy', that sold over 3 million. He found one "Top 10" and wrote one "Top 30" song for them. However, he only worked with them for one year . . . something about . . . 'they made him CRAZY' . . . but I have invaded his dreams on several occasions this last year and all he says is "I'm done, used up, consumed, empty, depleted and drained, so find someone else to entrance and beguile you 'space winney' . . . and 'wonder of wonders', for some strange reason, he's started to end some of his words with 'eth'. . . just like you!!"

"Hmmmmmmm. . . ." grinned the BIG SPIRIT. "He still bears watching . . ."

And the Angels sang:
        Buddy can you spare a dime
        For a little glass of wine
        Buddy don't you pity me
        Just one drink
        Then I'll be
        In a world all my own
        The only place I call home
        Where no hurt can get to me
        Where no one but me can see

        Pretty flowers dance and sing
        Laughter is a common thing
        Where no hate has ever been
        'Cause I won't let it in
        By the warm purple flame
        Ever little grape calls my name
        As it climbs on the fire
        And makes the fire burn higher

        Higher than it's ever been
        Time and space mean nothing then
        I fall about a mile or two
        So pardon me if I ask you
        Buddy can you spare a dime
        For a little glass of wine

Song: "First Street Blues" – Lee Hazlewood ©

THANKS GUYS. . . . . . .
I'LL TAKE IT FROM HERE . . .L.H.

IN ANOTHER DAY, in another time, in a city we shall call Los Angeles (to protect the names of the guilty), when radio stations were playing three Beatle records every ten minutes and keeping this piece of ridiculousness going twenty-four hours a day, I quit the record business. I quit all business. I retired.

I retired to my backyard. I played my guitar. I watched bugs swim in my pool. I talked to my wife (I was married in those days, but I believe if the world can forgive Japan for Pearl Harbor, I should be able to forgi . . . well, maybe not). I timed my bodily functions so as to cause little or no disturbance to the bugs or my Chivas Regal drinking. I talked to my children and asked them not to fall in the pool and dirty it for the bugs. (I liked them bugs.) I was a happy man. Retired in my early thirties with enough eggs in my little nest to carry me, providing the bugs took good care of the pool and kept repair bills to a minimum. BUT the best laid plans of bugs and retired record producers often . . .

Once upon a sunny summer afternoon my next-door neighbor, one Jimmy Bowen, 'ex-teenage idol', gainfully employed record producer for Reprise Records, stuck his head over my six-foot wall and while looking through the double strand of electric barbed wire said, "Hello".

I did not return his greeting with any great haste. I was, I assure you, not searching for an answer; it was more a question of disturbing the bugs and sharing my scotch. Since Jimmy knew of my retirement, which had lasted eight months thus far; I felt a certain resentment in his 'nine-to-five' eyes. He was, however, a much younger man and more able to cope with the problems of gainful employment. His artist roster read like a "Who's Who" in the record business . . . Frank Sinatra, Dean Martin, Sammy Davis Jr., etc . . . and with names like that he could well afford to sing 'Fuck the Beatles" in any key. Somehow I sensed envy in his visual accusations of my doing nothing. Doing nothing! Riding herd on a restless band of swimming bugs, making long trips to the house for ice and clean glasses. You call that nothing? He called THAT nothing! Still, I forgave him, for youth is not a crime, though it should be. I filled my glass slowly and answered his hello with a less than interested "Hi".

I knew in an instant this was a mistake, for a micro-second later he had cleared the wall with a single bound, ran to my bottle, poured what I thought was an unnecessarily large drink and seated himself next to my person.

"Barton," he said, calling me by my maiden name, "it's time you got off your ass and did something."

"James," said I, in a mature voice garnished with fatherly understanding made possible by my being six years his senior, "not thirty minutes ago I WAS off my ass . . . off my ass getting more ice."

"But you've got to do more, Barton."

"Oh, I did, James, I did!"

"You did!" he screamed.

I put my arm around his Reprise shoulders and continued, "I did, James. The phone rang and I answered it."

"You didn't!"

"I just told you I did, my boy, but it was a mistake."

"Who was it?" he queried breathlessly.

"It was Jack Tracy, from Mercury Records, daring to suggest I end my retirement. He offered me a job!"

"You didn't accept!!"

"No. I was very kind, however."

"Oh, pray tell me, what did you do?"

"I simply explained he had a wrong number and hung up."

"But let that be a lesson to me, James," I went on, "I'll never answer the phone again unless I'm quite positive 'Dialing for Dollars' is calling." ('Who Wants To Be A Millionaire" was still a dream in 1964).

"You can't spend the rest of your goddamn life watching fucking bugs!"

"You're right, James," I replied, "I plan to spend an equal part watching bugs fuck. I'm a voyeur," I confessed, "plain and simple. It's a weakness for which there is no cure. I've been saddled with this secret for years and now you've found me out. Here, have some more ice, young James."

"No, I'll take another drink."

"I was afraid of that."

Jimmy drank that drink and several more and with a certain corpse-like redness in his eyes (a common ailment in those who must spend at least eight of their waking hours engaged in toil), he explained his predicament.

It seems our hero had fallen in love or something with one Nancy Sinatra and she with him. This I found desirable, since I felt she surely could afford his drinking habits, which I certainly could not. He went on to explain since their lust for each other had begun, he had started producing her records. He further related she had had several producers before him and none including himself could get her anything that remotely resembled a selling record. Her last recording, he insisted, had sold only ten copies but somehow Reprise record distributors had returned seventeen. Even I thought this a bit strange.

He had, as I suspected, (two bottles earlier) come to enlist my aid. He knew my answer before the 'no' left my senior citizen lips. James pleaded, he begged, he cried and he also scared the bugs. He promised everything, including money . . . and then, 'dear reader', he rang the bell.

He actually promised to replenish my diminishing supply of Chivas. He promised all of this if I would just meet with the lady and casually discuss the possibility, of the possibility, of writing a couple songs for her and perhaps, maybe, in the far distant future, consider the remoteness of my possibly coming out of retirement, to produce one single 45 rpm two-sided disc with a Nancy Sinatra singing on both sides, maybe.

I am, 'dear reader', basically a weak man who on occasion has shed tears at a well-executed card trick or Shirley Temple singing "On the Good Ship Lolli-pop". So in my moment of weakness, and to quiet the bugs grown restless from the emotional outburst of young Jimmy, I whimpered a definite, possible, maybe for a meeting the following Tuesday night.

James, limp and spent, stumbled away, a tear drenched shadow of his former self. The bugs settled down for the night and I went to the house for more ice.

THE FIRST OF
MANY SUMMIT MEETINGS

THE FOLLOWING TUESDAY EVENING, with some small assistance from my dog Trouble, a one hundred sixty-five pound Great Dane, (she drove), we arrived at the Beverly Hills address of Nancy Sinatra who was living at the time with her mother, Nancy Sinatra Sr. (This should be a very important historical fact and add great depth and dimension to our story, but somehow it loses some of its' shock value in the telling.)

I was greeted at the door by a rather short, fleet of foot, handsome child who stated almost immediately, "Hello, Dummy. I'm Nancy with the laughing face. Ha ha ha," as she danced small erratic figure eights around me and my well-worn guitar case.

"Oh. Gee whiz. Golly . . . that's swell," I belted dramatically and entered the house. Trouble stayed in the car and listened to Beatle records.

The first thing I noticed, on entering, was several Chivas Regal bottles placed strategically around the rooms. 'What a warm home', I thought. The second thing I noticed placed strategically around the rooms were some people.

There was one Bobby Darin (Italian singer; one Rona Barrett (still allowed in the house in those days); one James Darren (Italian TV Star); one Billy Strange (hillbilly guitar picker) – who claimed to be an arranger – a fact he proved quite admirably several times after this meeting; one Jimmy Bowen (Reprise-dressed and Chivas-drinking record producer), and another rather nice looking gentleman who introduced himself as Frank Sinatra, and after checking his drivers license and several credit cards, I accepted this fact quite readily.

Bobby Darin was seated at the piano 'singing up all the songs HE ever knew'. I approached him with some caution for I was afraid if I showed the least interest, he would 'sing up all the songs I ever knew'. My caution was not a deterrent, however, for he quickly sang three hundred unforgettable songs I had forgotten, and then for his twenty-third encore jumped on the piano and whistled three choruses of "Rebel Rouser", a multi-million selling, Duane Eddy single from 1958.

I felt a startling sharp pain from a punch to my left kidney, and turned to notice the rather short girl, her face still laughing.

"Do you find me humorous?" I queried.

"No, Dummy, I'm Nancy with the laughing face. Ha ha ha," said she, pirouetting away.

Holding my slightly bruised kidney, I crawled over and lay myself next to Jimmy Bowen.

"Does her face always laugh?"

"Always," young James answered, tilting a Chivas bottle in my direction.

"Don't you find this strange?"

"The only thing I find strange in this house is HIM," Jim answered, pointing to Billy.

"It's okay," I stated, "I invited him. He says he's an arranger."

"He says he can play guitar too," James retorted, "but look at that right hand. Now, even you will have to admit, Barton" James continued, "Two toes, three thumbs and one finger is not what you normally find on the right hand of your average guitar player."

"I never said he was average, James, and I do agree with you. It's one toe too many!"

Jimmy turned away in apparent disgust, and from the next room we heard, "I'm Nancy with the laughing face. Ha ha ha."

"How can one make records with a girl whose face laughs constantly?" I wondered aloud.

"With that Strange guitar picker you shouldn't have any trouble," answered an arrogant Jimmy. "And how's your dog? Is she still chauffeuring for you, you cheap bastard?"

"Yes, she is," I replied hastily, "but my financial conservativeness is not the topic of discussion this evening. What's more important is how is it possible to make records with a lady whose face laughs constantly?"

"Now, 'ole buddy, you're beginning to see the problem."

"But James," I cried, "I've written for her a tender ballad concerning a young Israeli soldier who is dishonorably discharged from the Armed Services for putting a Cadillac engine in his World War II surplus Sherman tank. It's called 'So Long Abe'."

"Why don't you call it "So Long Babe'? Ha ha ha," said Nancy, dancing by.

I looked at James, James looked for another bottle of Chivas, Bobby stopped singing, Jimmy Darren did a soliloquy from 'The Colgate Comedy Hour', Billy Strange scratched his ass and gained three pounds, Nancy's mother served spaghetti sandwiches, Rona Barrett wrote it all down, Frank put on Billy Stranges' raincoat and left saying, "Listen to the kid, dummy. It ain't such a bad idea."

It wasn't such a bad idea. Nancy sold 50,000 records, made the Billboard chart for the first time at number 80, and I went back to my bugs with six cases of hard-earned Chivas Regal.

THIS BOOT IS MADE FOR WALKING

NOW YOU WOULD THINK, 'dear reader', after temporarily coming out of retirement to secure the aforementioned young lady ONE _small_, happy hit record – a thing she had not had before – I would be left to find happiness with my dog and bugs in the sanctuary of my backyard . . . but no! THE BASTARDS WON'T LEAVE YOU ALONE!

"Let me live in peace!" I screamed one warm November day of the same year, when James Bowen again vaulted my fence, poured himself three times too much Chivas and said, "I am proud of you, Barton. You've done what no other man has done."

"Pigeon balls, James," said I, quickly taking his glass and downing one-half the content therein.

"Why are you so filled with anger?" James asked. "You are a national hero. Be proud, young warrior, for this day you are the captain of the universe. You've succeeded where greater men have failed. You have written and produced a record with the ridiculous title 'So Long Babe', and in doing so have given one Nancy Sinatra her first small hit. Oh, that I were in your shoes."

"You are being quite niggardly about the entire episode." I said, drinking the rest from his glass.

"We mustn't speak in that manner when talking about the woman I was once in love of," said James.

"Once in love of?"

"Yes, for now I plan to spend my time in the tee-pee of Keely Smith, Indian Princess and true love of my life."

"But James, I thought your heart beat for the Italian Maiden with the laughing face?"

"Barton, when you live in your backyard, thinking only of bugs and such," spake young James, "how can you possibly know the ways ones passions can be spent in the supermarkets of love?"

"Her father's gonna shoot a very big hole in your head!"

"Fear not. Her father approves of my Indian romance," saideth James, "for he is a just man. Besides, he doesn't think I'm good enough for her."

"I agree with her father."

"See," spake James, "you are a proud and just man too!"

"Screw thee, James. It's quite obvious you have come this day to weaken me with your Reprise-coated compliments."

"Barton, be kind. For I come unto you and ask this simple question. What have you written for the child to record next?"

"NEXT! Again I say pigeon balls, James, for I have yet to recover from the LAST! Did you know I had to threaten her with bodily harm to stop that insane laughter?"

"You didn't!"

"Yes I did!"

"You didn't strike the Pope's Daughter, did you? For if you did, I do this day have great fear for your well being."

"No, I didn't. I only threatened . . . ah . . . THE POPE'S DAUGHTER???"

"Yes," James said matter-of-factly, "all we very hip folk at Reprise Records refer to Frank Sinatra as the Pope, and Nancy being his daughter quite naturally is called . . . it's very 'in'. You should say 'it' sometime, Barton. It wouldn't hurt you to hip yourself up a bit."

"James," I begged. "it sounds . . . well . . . sorta . . . sacrilegious."

"That's what makes it so hip. It's very v-e-r-y 'in'. Go ahead and try it."

Pillars of timidity swelled in my throat as I slowly pursed my lips and whispered, "The Pope."

"Not bad, but put a little more into it. Try again."

I formed my quivering lips . . ."THE POPE . . . THE POPE . . . THE POPE!"

"Good! Good!" smiled James, giving me a very hip tap on my shoulder.

"THE POPE! THE POPE! THE POPE!" I screamed, the sound dancing its way across my newly hipped tongue.

James put his arm around me and cautioned, "Not too much the first day. Anyway, Barton, we must discuss business. Again I ask, what have you written for the lady with the laughing face?"

"Nothing! Nothing! Leave me alone!"

"But 'ole pal, buddy, comrade, friend . . . one cannot make just one small hit and stop. One must hold ones head high and go on to greater things."

"Double fuck-you, James," roared I in my most permanently retired voice, "I am finished. Through! Done! Do you understand, my simple ex-teenage idiot . . . er . . . idol?"

"But you forget one thing, friend of mine. Your business manager and accountant, Marvin Zolt, with full power of attorney, has signed a contract on your behalf, which states that should ONE Barton Lee Hazlewood secure ONE small hit for ONE Nancy Sinatra, with the laughing face, then ONE Barton Lee Hazlewood must write and or produce her records for at least ONE full year thereafter, etc."

"James, you're an asshole!"

"That may be," sayeth James, "but a contract is a contract and it must be honored. The show must go on. Buy Bonds. Don't be a litterbug, etc."

"If Trouble, my one hundred sixty-five pound Great Dane, were of a violent nature I would surely have her attack you this instant."

"Tsk, tsk, tsk," James lisped, "surely even you whose constant thoughts are of fowls' testicles realize justice will triumph all, never take a wooden nickel, and always remember the Alamo, etc. Don't you agree?" spake a delirious James Bowen, pouring himself another glass of my precious scotch.

I quickly wrestled the glass from his greedy Reprise hand and drank it dry.

"You are sometimes difficult, often lazy and surely the most stingy man I know," young James belched in rebuttal.

"And you drink too much," I stated.

"Not in this house I don't!!"

"Well, you TRY to drink too much and your feet stink and you don't love Roy Rogers and several other things that escape me for the moment."

"Oh well, no matter," said James, "let us talk more of the business at hand. What have you written?"

"I have no new songs and I don't expect to have any, James!"

"Then record an old one. Now let's see . . ." he whispered, picking up my writers notebook and thumbing his way through my very soul.

"What about this one," he asked. " 'Take My Love And Shove It Up Your . . . ' . . . er . . . no, I don't think her public is quite ready for that. Ah Ha! What's this one? It doesn't seem to have a title."

"It's none of your business," I bellowed, grabbing the manuscript and clutching it to my heart.

"It must be good or you wouldn't be so protective."

"Good? It's beautiful! It's a haunting ballad of a young Southerner just returned from our great Civil War. He is being carried on a stretcher by two of his buddies for his left leg has been bitten off by a very large Northern prostitute named 'Big Philadelphia'. It tells of his hurt and embarrassment at not being able to walk, and while pointing to his one remaining foot, he cries the title in his noticeably strained Southern baritone voice, 'This Boot Is made For Walking'."

James sat in silence shaking his head, tears flowing.

"Well, what do you think, my boy?" asked I, pride nearly bursting the seams of my shirt.

"I think the telephone is ringing," he answered, wiping his tears on an old Chivas label.

"Don't answer it!" I screamed

"Why not?"

"It might be somebody!"

"Well, of course it's somebody, Barton. Why else would it ring?" he said, picking up the phone.

"Give me that," I yelled, taking it from him and brushing the cobwebs from the receiver.

"Hello, dummy. It's me. Ha ha ha. Why don't you call it 'These Boots Are Made For Walking'?" said a voice from the phone.

"How could she possibly know?" I said, looking at James and covering the receiver with my hand.

"I know, dummy . . . I know," came the voice from the phone. "Ha ha ha. Bye bye."

I put the receiver back in its dusty cradle and looked to James for council.

"Sinatras have 20-20 hearing. They hear good, don't they, Barton?"

"Good? Jeeeeezsus, James, its twenty miles to Beverly Hills! Why, even Trouble has difficulty hearing all the words on a Beatle record!"

Trouble blushed at my disclosure, got up, walked over and peed rather distastefully in my pool.

"She could hear better if she didn't drink so much," young James mused.

"Nancy drinks too much?"

"No, Trouble," he answered.

"My dogs' drinking habits are not your concern. She had an unhappy childhood and . . ."

The phone rang again. I quickly put it to my ear.

"Listen to the kid, dummy. It ain't such a bad idea!" a voice chimed from the phone.

An all-knowing Jimmy poured himself another glass of Chivas Regal. I drank it. Trouble turned on the radio. The bugs swam to 'Hold My Hand'. Nancy recorded my beautiful 'These Boots Are Made For

Walking' (with a few slight changes in the lyric) and the sonofoabitchin' record sold five million copies 'round the world. Yes, 'dear reader', Nancy with the laughing face, 'ha ha ha', was off and running and my retirement was reduced to a dream.

THE DAY BEFORE "D"-DAY

AS I DROVE THROUGH THE GATES of my North Hollywood Ledge Avenue retreat, strange and wonderful moans filled the afternoon air.

"Barton! Barton! Barton Lee!"

"How can I pleasure you?" I asked, easily recognizing the voice of my friend, guitar virtuoso and permanent guesthouse guest, Donnie Owens.

"Well, for one thing, you can call your one hundred sixty-five pound 'brown whore'."

"You're speaking of Trouble, I presume."

"You bet your sweet ass I am. She's got me pinned to the bed again!"

"She <u>love</u>th you, Donald," I sang.

"Why can't she love me like any other dog? Lick my hand or my . . . oh . . . oh, Barton!"

"She's not like other dogs, Donald."

"True! Oh, so true! Do you realize she's been humping me for the past four hours?"

"That long, huh? It's undoubtedly a new record. Perhaps we should call the Olympic Committee . . ."

"Barton! Please! Please call your 'brown whore'".

"Oh, very well, Donald. Trouble . . . oh . . . Trou—ble. Bring Uncle Donald and come to the pool. Daddy's made you a nice drinkie'."

I heard a thunderous bark of joy, and looking to the right noticed my 'beauty' jumping the fence surrounding the guesthouse with a well-loved Donnie Owens dangling from her mouth. She dropped him at my feet. Donald arose brushing the slobbers of love from his seersucker robe and exclaimed, "I've had it. I mean I really had it this time. Four hours! Four fucking hours, and I do mean Fucking hours, Barton!!"

"She loves you, Donald!"

"I don't want her love! I'm a married man! I'm not sure, but I may have committed adultery this afternoon!!!"

"My lips are sealed, Donald. Your bride, Bernice, will never know . . ."

"I was just lying there on the bed, reading what the critic for the Farmer's Almanac had to say about 'These Boots Are Made For Walking', when that big 'brown whore' came romping through the door and attacked me. Attacked me, do you hear?!!!"

"Did the critic like the record?"

"No more than I liked what was happening to me!"

"Now, quiet yourself, Donald, and remember 'love is a many splendored thing'. You know," I mused, "that's her favorite film."

A sighing Trouble nodded in agreement.

"Then for godssake, get her a television set. It's been showing three times a day! Get her anything, but get her away from me! Away, you hear? Away!!

Trouble finished her drink, walked poolside and gazed longingly. The bugs were gone. Winter had come and they, like all God's creatures, had found their way to Palm Springs.

"By the way," an almost calm Donald said, 'Nancy with the laughing face, ha ha ha, called while you were away. Congratulations! You are going to Europe tomorrow."

"I am going nowhere tomorrow!"

"She said you'd say that."

"She did?"

"Yes, and she also said I should tell you to 're-member the contract, etc.'."

"Donald, is it true you take sadistic pleasure in my sorrows? You don't happen to know WHY I'm going to Europe tomorrow?"

"Well, now that you mention it . . . it seems Re-prise Records believes an in-person tour, by Nancy with the laughing face and you, will increase the sales of future records."

"But it's cold in Europe in February, Donald. I've seen all those war movies . . . I remember John Wayne . . . standing with ice in his beard . . ."

"Makes little difference. Your plane leaves to-morrow at 8 a.m. I packed your suitcase. Don't worry about a thing.

I touched the hem of his seersucker robe say-ing, "Donald, taketh good care of Trouble whilst I'm away."

"I will, Barton. I plan to put her in a kennel."

"That would be cruel, for she loves you so."

"Go to hell, Barton."

"Thank you, Donald. I'll bet it's warmer than Europe in February."

EUROPE ON $$$$$ A DAY

THE LOS ANGELES INTERNATIONAL AIRPORT was wet and windy the following morning. Just like in the John Wayne movies.

"Well, I see you made it, dummy. Ha ha ha," said 'guess who' on my arrival.

"Yes, but know this, young Italian lady . . . I make this trip under duress. However, it is nice to see so many have come to witness our departure." Sayeth me.

"Witness our departure? They're going with us!" challenged Nancy.

"All these people?" questionedeth me.

"Just cool it , dummy. Reprise is paying. Besides, I like company." Whispered her.

"Pigeon poon," thought me, glancing at our entourage.

There was Mama Sinatra, with several Frito Snack Pacs strapped to her back. There was Billy Strange, magnetic arranger. There was Eddie Brackett, sterling recording engineer, with 'God Bless America' streamers flying from his U.S. Army 'lucky' fatigue cap. There was a man with fifty-three (count 'em) cameras around his neck with the name Ron Joy stenciled on each in illuminous chartreuse lettering. There was little 'Ha ha ha' and ME.

"... and now, Ladies and Gentlemen," the young man from the airline lisped, "if you will just follow me, we will board the plane."

Fifty-three flashbulbs (count 'em) exploded simultaneously on fifty-three cameras (count 'em) temporarily blinding us all. Bravely we held hands and were led onto the plane.

"I'm blind! I'm blind!" screamed Me.

"Well, sober up. We're leaving." said Mama.

"There's ice in my moustache!" shivered Me.

"You know, you look a little like John Wayne when you're angry." confessed Nancy.

"I think one of my 'God Bless America' streamers is on fire!" barked Eddie B., sterling engineer.

"Can I stand next to you and melt my ice?" Me wondered aloud.

"I wonder if I brought enough batons?" burped Billy Strange, magnetic arranger.

"Father, Son and Holy Ghost." The pilot, dropping to his knees announced.

"... wonder if I brought enough flashbulbs?" sighed, Ron Joy.

"GOD, I HOPE NOT!" screeched all.

"I like holding hands." jested Her.

"You're holding my moustache." confessed Me.

"Oh, sorry." Confessed Her.

"That's alright. I kinda liked it." double confessed Me.

Ha ha ha." chortled Her.

"AMEN" sangeth all

ROME

"SO THIS IS PARIS!" dappled Eddie B., sterling engineer.

"No, idiot, its . . ."

"The Pope lives around here someplace." flashed Ron Joy.

"I didn't know Frank had a house in Rome." whole-noted Billy S., magnetic arranger.

"My God! There's ice in my moustache!" frenzied Me.

"You look like a short John Wayne when you're crying." acceded Mama.

"Look at that old ruin" pronounced Me.

"You don't look so good yourself, young man." zagged the old ruin.

"Never saw so goddamn many sports cars." echoed Eddie B., sterling engineer.

"Wonder where we can buy some dirty pictures?" inquired Me.

"I think you get those in Germany." abutted Her.

"Somebody just pinched my ass." half-noted B.

Strange, magnetic arranger.

"Oh, sorry."

"That's all right. I sorta liked it." quarter-noted B. Strange, magnetic arranger.

"How about some Italian food?" questioned Mama.

"Yeah, a good cheeseburger and some homefries!" 1/8-noted B. Strange, magnetic arranger.

"This looks like a good place." flickered Ron Joy

"Yes, look at all the trucks parked out front." reverbed Eddie B., sterling engineer.

"Whata 'ya mean, no HOMEFRIES?" belched Billy S., magnetic arranger.

"Watch it, will ya? You just poured catsup on one of my 'God Bless America' streamers!" intimated Eddie B., sterling engineer.

"I wonder if the Pope will bless my batons?" sixteenth-noted B. Strange, magnetic arranger.

"I'll bless your baton!" gagged Me.

"Biggest damn church I've ever seen. Listen to the echo. EYIOOOOO! YEIOOOOO! Oh, sorry lady!" driveled Eddie B., sterling engineer.

"That's all right. I kinda liked it."

"Look! The Palace of Caesar!" observed Mama.

"The one in Las Vegas is better." scintillated Ron Joy.

"Wanta-buy-some-dirty-pictures?"

"No. I think I'll wait 'til we get to Germany." animated Me.

"Look at the boobs on that one!" resounded Eddie B., sterling engineer.

"Those Romans really knew how to make a statue." flared Ron Joy.

Fantastic, huh?" asketh Me.

"What is it?" 32nd-noted B. Strange, magnetic arranger

"A genuine copy of Mussolini's uniform." boasted Me.

"You look a lot like Mussolini when you're happy." rewound Eddie B., sterling engineer

"I'm going to put it on this evening, have a few drinks and attack the Ethiopian commando in the room next to mine." bragged Me.

"Sounds like fun. Maybe I'll put on my Roman helmet with the big ostrich feather and join you." 64th-noted Billy S., magnetic arranger

"I'll see if she has a sister." breathed Me.

"What the hell is a Pouchi?" flickered Ron Joy.

"Some kind of little dog, I think." jousted Me.

"You know the trouble with Rome, don't ya?" Mama wisely asked.

"Yeah!" said all.

PARIS

"SO THIS IS GERMANY!"

"Take us to the George Five Hotel, and hurry, driver!" drawled Me.

"That's cinq! Cinq! Cinq!" sangeth Ha Ha Ha.

"Isn't the hotel beautiful?" chimed Mama

"I like the one at Disneyland better." flared Ron Joy.

"Look! I just bought a gallon of perfume for two Francs!" inebriated Me.

"What kind?" tuned B. Strange, magnetic arranger.

"I don't know. I can't read French." nincompooped Me.

"Let me see. 'Urine de Chaval' . . . sounds good." harmonized B. Strange, magnetic arranger.

"Are your accommodations satisfactory?" frenched Pierre P Pierre, 2nd assistant consierge.

"What?"

"Let me put it another way. Do you like your rooms?" frenched Andre A. Andre, gran consierge.

"Oh yes. I spend each evening watching the friendly French ladies from my windows. They give rides to strangers in their Mercedes and Jaguars." frizzled Me.

"They ain't so friendly. Look what one gave me!"

"Put that back in your pants! You're giving me a superiority complex."

"Maybe they're used car saleswomen?" twinkled Ron Joy.

"Room service ain't shit!" rang Eddie B., sterling engineer.

"Yeah. No HOMEFRIES!" aired B. Strange, magnetic arranger.

"Bridget Bardot wants to record two of my songs." melodiced Me.

"I didn't know she spoke English." sopranoed Ha Ha Ha.

"With Lee's songs it won't matter." parroted Eddie B., sterling engineer.

"Isn't that Peter O'Toole?"

"I don't like the crap suzettes." mouthed Me.

"I believe they're called 'crepes'." suggested Mama

"You better taste 'em." recanted Me.

"I see what you mean." smiled Mama.

"That Eiffel Tower is a mother!" orchestrated B. Strange, magnetic arranger.

"Look at the boobs on that tall one." flared Ron Joy.

"That mother is an Eiffel." juggled Me.

"I just bought three hundred and fifty-seven new dresses and a see-through bra." euphamized Ha Ha Ha.

"I just bought a solid gold egg timer. I can't lift the damn thing." spoketh Me.

"Ha ha ha."

"What's she laughing at now?" twinkled Ron Joy.

"The sign in the ladies' john. Look at Charles De Gaulles' feet".

"My Uncle Cuckold's wife had three children when he was over eighty." confessed B. Strange, magnetic arranger

"There's ice in my . . ."

"You know, you look like a short John Wayne when you're very cold." chilled Mama.

"So I'm short. Napoleon was short." squatted Me.

"But he didn't write silly songs." harmonized Ha Ha Ha.

"Well, fuck him then!"

"Have you been to the Louvre?" cross-examined Mama.

"I don't have to go right now. Ask me later." pleaded Me.

"I just bought two thousand and six pairs of shoes and a see-through yo-yo." pirouetted Ha Ha Ha.

" . . . and charged it all to Reprise records."

"Can you imagine a hat with 'God Bless France' printed right on it?" taped Eddie B., sterling engineer.

"Disgraceful!

"You know what's wrong with France?" beseeched Mama.

"Yeah" <u>said</u>eth all.

HAMBURG

"SO THIS IS . . ."

"Shish! I told Lee it was Stockholm."

"Ha ha ha."

"What's she laughing at now?"

"She's laughing at Hamburgers and Lee doesn't know where we are."

"Would you look at that hat! 'God Bless Germany'!?!" reverberated Eddie B., sterling engineer for the 2nd time.

"Look at all those kids," expounded Me.

"There must be ten thousand of 'em." quick counted B. Strange, magnetic arranger.

"They look friendly enough." deemed Mama.

"I'll just hit one and see."

"They don't look so friendly now." zoomed Ron Joy.

"What shall we do? We can't fight 'em all." reasoned Eddie B., sterling engineer

"I'm going to surrender." limped Me.

"No you're not, you traitor. Take that **%%##!

And this %%##**$!#!" slugged B. Strange, magnetic arranger.

"You looked just like John Wayne when you knocked the ice off Lee's moustache." grinned Mama.

"Here come the police. Maybe they'll help." gargled Me.

"They look friendly enough." improvised Ha Ha Ha

"I'll just hit one and see . . ."

LONDON

"TO THE HILTON HOTEL and hurry, driver!"

"Wot?"

"I don't think he understood you." hampered Me.

"He speaks English, doesn't he?" stormed Mama.

"Yes, but not American." quaffed Me.

"Here, let me try it. 'Ta us to the 'ilton 'otel and 'urry, driver!" tutored B. Strange, magnetic arranger

"Right you are, gov'."

"Nobody like a smart ass!" flared Ron Joy.

"We have reservations for everyone in your party but a Mr. 'azlewood." spit Barnard Brit, professional middle class Englishman

"It figures."

"Don't you worry, Lee. Young man, let me speak to the manager!" grunted Mama.

"Lay it on him, Mama."

"Yes, Madam, may I be of some assistance?"

'Yes' thought me 'die this instant you brit twit'.

"Look! You have just fifteen minutes to get Mr.

Hazlewood a nice suite or we all move!" so sayeth Ha Ha Ha's Ma Ma Ma.

"That's telling him, Mama!"

"Very well, Madam, to what hotel shall I have your luggage sent?"

"You mean. . . ?"

"Yes, Madam. There is not one extra suite in the inn, but I'm sure we can find something for Mr. Hazlewood in the manger." Titled Brit Twit

"Jeeeeezsus! The manger!" moaned Ha Ha Ha.

"Where's Lee going?" inquired Mama.

"Outside to look at the sky."

"Wait 'til the Pope hears about this." 8 tracked Eddie B., sterling engineer.

"He's got enough problems trying to get his see-through yo-yo back." spaketh old weak battery, Ron Joy.

"How do you like living in the manger?" inquired luxury living Ha Ha Ha.

"It's not a manger. It's just a small room. A very, very small room." cried Me.

"You've worn the same suit the entire trip." stated B. Strange, magnetic arranger.

"Yes, I know." wept Me.

"Lose your luggage?"

"No. Donnie Owens packed my bag. One suit and seventy three pairs of argyle socks."

"A man should take care of his feet." related B. Strange, magnetic arranger.

"Oh, I do . . . change socks three times a day."

"What'll we do tonight?" glistened Ron Joy.

"Let's go somewhere warm and watch Lee's moustache melt.'

"Let's go buy some soap for the maids.'

"Let's go throw rocks at the Beatles."

"Don't nobody go nowhere! We are making an album tonight!" Ha Ha Ha tantrumed.

"Oh, puma poon. Nobody told me we had to work." slinked Me.

"I thought this was a reward for making that stupid 'Boots' record?" frolicked Me in another key.

"It is, Dummy, but we're going to make some more stupid records.'

"Where is Lee going?"

"Back to the manger."

"Where are we going?"

"Outside to look at the sky."

"This is a good recording studio? repeating echoed Eddie B., sterling engineer.

"That sounded like a question."

"It was."

"Is Billy conducting with the baton the Pope blessed?" clicked Ron Joy.

"Just on Italian songs."

"Not another goddamn tea break!" damned B. Strange, magnetic arranger.

"English musicians sit funny, don't they?"

"God, listen to that vocal group. They sing worse than Lee."

"I didn't know Lee sang." minimized Mama

"Not since he defrosted his moustache."

"What'll we call the album?" comatosed Ron Joy.

" 'Nancy in London' ain't a bad name." smiled Me.

"It isn't a good one,"

"Then it's settled. We'll call it 'Nancy in London'." pronounced Ha Ha Ha.

"Let's go home." <u>said</u>eth all.

"I've lost a camera." teared Ron Joy

"Christ, now he only has fifty-two (count 'em)."

"Billy Strange just got a telegram from the Pope."

"What did he want?"

"Probably wants the batons back."

"Goodbye, Merry 'ole England!"

"Goodbye, all you nice boobies." smiled Me.

"I think you mean Bobbies.'

"Leave me alone. I know exactly what I mean." tittered me.

"Ha ha ha."

"Father, Son and Holy Ghost." Sang some.

"AMEN" sang all.

THE HOMECOMING

"WELCOME HOME, BARTON," spoke my virus-complected friend, Donald Owens. "Much has happened since last we stood together and smoked the pipe of contentment,"

"Contentment, your ass, Donald," sayeth I, "just look at this suit that doubtfully adorns my semi-perfect self! Look!!!"

"A little frayed at the knees perhaps, but I find little fault with the fabric or the cut," wheezed Donald. "Though you've never been a pillar of tonsorial splendor, I feel one of your small stature easily blends into the background and offends practically no one . . . except perhaps –"

"Donald. . . !"

"Yes, Barton?"

"Stop! Terminate!! Stay!!! Let not another participle dangle from your country and western lips. Did you know I've been wearing the same 'mother-loving' suit for three weeks?"

"Whatever for?" Donald catechized. "You have

several rather nice ones I've worn on many occasions and have found them to be adequate. Mind you, they're not in tune with my personal tastes. Still —"

"Donald!!!"

"Yes, Barton?"

"Hush!!"

"Very well, if that would please you."

"It would, Donald. It would! Now, I'm going to ask you 'uno' question. I want your answer to be as brief as possible. "Do you understand?"

"Most assuredly, Barton."

"Very well. Now, Donald," I asked through the tight lips on my thermometer-red face, "What possessed you to pack my bag with one suit and seventy-three pairs of argyle socks?"

"Well, I supposed that would be quite obvious to a multi-talented individual such as yourself," he replied quite snobbishly.

"No, Donald. It was not!"

"I can see that. Well, it should have been," Donald frowned, dismissing the subject, quickly opening the door and escorting me into the house.

"Notice anything different?" Donald joyously asked, flashing his simulated Charlie Brown smile.

I carefully scrutinized my home. Everything seemed the same. Half a ham sandwich lay on the dining room table, just as it had the day I took my leave.

"My ham sandwich has turned green?"

"No, but you're getting warm," Donald grinned.

"Trouble is pregnant?"

"No, but she's getting warmer," Donald simpered.

"James Bowen stopped drinking?"

"No, but you're really getting warmer." Donald smirked.

"Well, what is it, for christsakes!!!"

"Your wife and children have moved out." Donald smiled.

"What!" screamed I. "When did that happen?"

"About two weeks before you left for Europe," he said, hardly repressing his titters.

"Why didn't someone tell me? Why is the husband the last to know? Oh, where did I go wrong?"

"Well, starting back in 1952," Donald convulsingly gagged, "you were –"

"Never mind, you don't have to start at the beginning!! What I want to know is, where did I go wrong recently?"

"It would be a lot easier if I told you where you went right." Donald laughed with priggish mirth, placing his arm around my heavy burdened ex-husband shoulders.

"All right!! Then where have I gone right recently?"

"No where," tenuous Donald rasped, "no where!!"

"You're cruel, inhuman, brutal and merciless," I slurped, wavering into my red velvet bedroom and slamming my broken spirited body on silken sheets. "I need sleep, Donald. Sleep and rest," ho-hummed me, "for I am suffering from acute jet-lag and terminal European toilet paper fatigue."

"There's some Ex-Lax and Vicks Vapor Rub on your nightstand," Donald offered, lowering his light frame to rest at the end of the bed.

"Donald, there are some things Ex-Lax and Vicks Vapor Rub will not cure . . . let attempt to explain . . . jet-lag is the time difference between L.A. and London, the gaining or forfeiting of eight hours. It has a decided negative effect on ones body, physically and mentally. You see, since the big jets have. . . . ."

I peered at Donald, but 'twas no use, for he had fallen asleep at my feet.

MAMA

"IT'S FOR YOU," Donald spoke, handing me the phone, "its Nancy's mama."

"Hello, Lee?'

"Hello, Mama."

"Hello, Lee?"

"Yes, Mama. It's me."

"How can I be sure?"

"Mama, believe me, it's me!"

"Are you sure?"

"I've never been more sure, mama. My wife has left me, my dog Trouble may be pregnant, I'm suffering from jet-lag diarrhea, my Japanese gardener Joe-Joe Run-Run has just tried to hang himself on a poison ivy vine because I wouldn't listen to a song he had written for your daughter, a not too easy feat since I recently had all the poison ivy vines transplanted in a neighbors yard to retaliate for his dog having bitten Trouble quite severely in the public region, and Jimmy Bowen, as a gesture of friendship, is having a giant gate cut in the six-foot wall separating our homes. Who else could it be? I ask you, Mama, who else?"

"Oh, you poor sonofabitch," spoke a kind, concerned Mama.

"Thank you, mama, thank you."

"Hello, Lee?'

"Yes, Mama, I'm still here."

"Now listen, Lee. I want to talk to you about something. Hello, Lee?"

"I'm still –"

"Shut up and listen, Lee. Now when you and my daughter make those ridiculous records late at night, tell me . . . who is in the studio?"

"Well, we usually send the band home early . . . that leaves Eddie Brackett, the engineer . . . Billy Strange, the arranger . . . Nancy, and myself."

"AH HA!!!"

"Do I detect a note of alarm in your voice, Mama?"

"Hello, Lee?"

"Yes, Mama."

"I want you to hire a guard for Nancy, should you work past sundown."

"May I inquire why, Mama?"

"You may dummy . . . because somebody might steal her . . . that's why!! Somebody stole her brother a couple of months ago and it took almost a week to get him back. I don't want no more of that garbage! You understand?"

"Hello, Lee?"

"Yes, Mama, I'm here. Well, if it will put your mind at ease, I'll certainly be happy to hire a guard."

"Good boy!"

"Hello, Lee?"

"Yes mama."

"What was the name of the song Joe-Joe Run-Run wrote for my daughter?"

"Well, I personally haven't heard it, but Donald says the Japanese translates roughly to 'How Does That Grab You, Sukiyaki'."

"Hello, Lee?"

"Yes, Mama."

"Change 'Sukiyaki' to 'Darling'. It might be okay then, Dummy."

"Thank you, mama."

"Por nada. Goodbye."

"Goodbye, Mama."

"Hello, Lee?"

"Goodbye, Mama."

"Goodbye, Lee."

'How Does That Grab You, Darling' sold 1,200,000 (worldwide).

A FEW MORE RECORDS
AND SOME AVERAGES

"ALL RIGHT, STRANGER. Make one false move and I'll plug you," spoke the three hundred fifty-pound; khaki dressed guard with the six iron on his hip, twenty-gallon hat on his head, and a star on his chest.

" I beg your pardon," stated me.

"Better watch it, Stranger, or I'm gonna fill you full of lead."

"Look, Farley, do you have any idea who or whom you're addressing?" I questioned.

"It don't make no difference, Stranger. This studio ain't big enough for the two of us."

"I'll say it ain't," I retorted. "You fat –"

"Don't let the size fool you, smart ass Stranger," spake the guard. "I'm as light on my feet as a sparrow, and that's my handle, Stranger . . . George Sparrow. And who might'n you be?"

"Well, I might be the silly sonofabitch that hired you!" I shouted. "I might be, and God knows, I am."

"Watch it, Grand Canyon Mouth, or you'll end up in Boot Hill."

"Look, Mr. Sparrow—"

"Call me 'Biggin' . . ."

"All right, 'Biggin', I'm Lee Hazlewood, I'm the idiot that hired you, I'm –"

"How do I know that, short, mustached, smart ass Stranger? I mean, for all I know, you might-a-come here to steal Miss Nancy and I'd get mighty riled if'n you laid a hand on that purdy little gal."

Suddenly the door sprang open and in danced Miss Nancy.

"Hi, Sparrow."

"Howdy, Miss Nancy," the guard answered. "Do you know this short, mustached, smart ass critter?" pointing to 'guess who'."

"Oh, that's Barton," Nancy said. "Hi, Barton."

"Howdy, Miss Nancy," spoke I.

"Look, Stranger, are you-a-making fun out of the way I talk?" asked the guard, sticking the barrel of his six gun up my left nostril.

"Oh no, Mr. Sparrow," sneezed I.

"Call me 'Biggin'."

"Okay, 'Biggin'. I was just trying to get in the mood of things."

"Well, you better watch it, short mustached, smart ass tenderfoot. Or I might kick up a little dust with ya." 'Biggin' Sparrow replied.

"Oh, he's all right, Sparrow," Nancy said. "He is a short, mustached, smart ass like you say, but he's all right."

"Well, if'n he bothers you, you just let me know. Huh? Miss Nancy?"

"Oh, I will . . . I will."

I walked half a city block around the left side of 'Biggin' Sparrow, and entered the recording booth of Studio B. The musicians had arrived several minutes earlier. In fact, my somewhat lengthy conversation with George 'Biggin' Sparrow made me ten minutes late, costing Reprise Records several hundred dollars. This waste of Reprises' money occupied my mind for several guilty seconds. Then I 'crossed' myself and thought, "Oh, fuck 'em."

Billy Strange, Arranger and Conductor sided up to my side saying "Jeeeeezsus, Barton! For some time now all of us have known you weren't a very good songwriter. We forgave you. I personally have never worked with a worse record producer. But I forgive you. I've never attached much importance to your little faults, like awkwardness and stupidity. But, jeeeeezsus, Barton –"

"What are you trying to say, William?"

"Well, jeeeeezsus, Barton, it seems any short, mustached asshole could get to a recording session on time!!"

"I was here in plenty of time, but 'Biggin' wouldn't let me – "

"Jeeeeezsus, Barton, jeeeeezsus, jeeeeezsus," Billy mumbled, walking back into the studio.

"And now, gentlemen, if we could quiet down, perhaps we could get started," I shouted over the intercom.

"Why won't they listen to me?" I asked looking to Eddie Brackett, our recording engineer.

"They won't listen because they can't hear you. And they can't hear you because I haven't turned the equipment on.

I will not turn the equipment on until you make your friend, Donald Owens, put every one of my 'God Bless America' streamers back on my genuine U.S. Army 'lucky' fatigue cap." Stormed an angry Eddie Brackett. "You short, moustached, shit-heel, just how—"

"What happened to 'smart ass'?" I interrupted.

"I don't like _that_ word." Eddie blared, continuing . . ."Just how would you like for me to call a strike? How would you like that? Huh?"

"Oh my God!! Not a strike!" I cried, running through the double doors into the studio. "Donald! Donald Owens!! For God sakes, give Eddie Brackett back his 'God Bless America' streamers."

"Why should I?" Donald asked.

"Because," I answered swiftly, catching my breath . . ."because, _number one_, he will not turn on the equipment until you do. _Number two_, he will call a strike and you will be out of work for months, causing your bride and many children to surely starve. And _number three_, because if you do not return them to him immediately, I shall have Billy Strange break every finger on your right and left hand and – "

"If it's multiple choice, I choose number three," a somewhat irritated Donald said.

"Good!" sang I.

Walking back into the booth with Donald, I inquired, "I'm almost afraid to ask why you took Eddies' 'God Bless America' streamer from his U.S. Army 'lucky' fatigue cap in the first place, but I must. Why did you take them??"

"Don't ask," Donald replied, shaking his head and returning the streamers to Eddie.

""Very well, then, I won't."

"Good!" Donald whimpered, walking back into the studio.

"Everything is turned on and ready to go!" a 'God Bless America' streamer-laden Eddie Brackett shouted.

"Fantastic! Now, Miss Sinatra and gentlemen, let us start this evening with the song entitled—"

"Take ten! Take ten!" shouted Dirt Lanier, contractor for the musicians.

"Take ten? How can they take ten? They haven't played one note yet. Not one lousy note!"

"Look, Barton," an unconcerned Union-minded Dirt Lanier stated, "we take a ten minute break every hour whether we play or not. Now if you don't like it, I can always call a strike."

"Oh my God!! Not a strike!! Take ten!" I pleaded, "TAKE A FIFTEEN IF YOU NEED IT!!!"

HA HA HA GETS DRAFTED

"BARTON," said Nancy with the laughing face, ha ha ha, "there's something I must tell you,"

"Yes, dear lady," spake me, shaking with interest and praying the Chivas Regal would not expire.

"Barton, I'm going to Viet Nam!"

"My God!" I choked, quickly emptying my glass. "You've been drafted! We're sending women now?" I questioned, adding hastily, "Look, just remember these things and you'll be all right. Always take a pro- phylactic kit with you when you go out on Saturday night. I was in Korea for 18 months and never caught anything but the trolley. And remember, don't blouse your trousers with rubbers . . . most company com- manders don't go for that. Don't volunteer for noth- ing and – "

"Silence, Dummy! I've not been drafted. The government has simply asked me to go and enter- tain the men."

"But what will you do?" I wondered aloud.

"Sing, of course!"

"Oh, sorry," replied me, "I nearly forgot."

"Now, I'm planning to take a few people with me. Who would you suggest?"

The silence that filled the room nearly ate the flowers off the wallpaper.

"Barton! Are you listening?"

"Oh, I was listening, dear lady. I was trying to think of someone I want to go to Viet Nam . . . I just can't think of a soul."

"How about yourself?" Ha ha ha inquired.

"Well," breathed me in five-four time, "I have at times, in yours and others' presence, shown certain inalienable death-wish tendencies. But know this to be true: while I positively love glory and fame, while I surely love money more than most, and while my love of Chivas Regal is known in at least forty countries, there is not enough of these aforementioned goodies on the face of this grand old globe that might get me to entertain the possibility of going to Viet Nam. And in closing, I would like to add, if I thought there was the remotest chance I might be subpoenaed for this little safari, I would this instant blow the great toes off both my right and left foots."

"You seem pretty definite, Barton."

"I'm glad you were able to surmise this from the subtleness of my words, dear lady."

"Oh well, no matter," said her, "just anybody who's anybody wants to go."

"Keen," spake me.

"What would you suggest I take with me?"

I pondered but a second and answered her, singing to the tune of 'The Twelve Days of Christmas':

"Twelve hand grenades a-boomin'"

"Eleven sub-machine guns a-dit-dit-dittin'"

"Ten M-1 rifles a-shootin'"
"Nine bombers a-bombin'"
"Eight forty-five pistols a-blappin'"
"Seven pair of combat boots a-runnin'"
"Six medics a-fixin'"
"Five 'kees a-smokin'"
"Four generals a-salutin'"
"Three senators a-bullshittin'"
"Two white flags a-wavin'"
"AND A BIG BOX OF THERMAL UNDER-WEAR"

"Barton! You're unpatriotic and you're drunk," Nancy stated with some sureness.

"Yes, my dear," said I, taking my best W.C. Fields' stance, "but tomorrow I'll be sober and . . ."

SISTER, BROTHER, DADDY

"WHILE NANCY AND HER GANG are hard at work at the Saigon Palace and many lesser Asian theatres, it has come to my attention you have started staying out past ten thirty p.m. and other forms of movie colony sinning." Stated Nancy's brother, Frank, changing tuxedoes without losing a stroke.

"Tis true words you speak, Mr. S." confessed I, "but remember, it wasn't me who started that 'ole crazy Asian war'." I adjusted my 'Kenny Rogers and the First Edition, featuring Terry Williams' glasses and continued, "and with your sister on the front lines, I have even found time to visit this most wonderful city of New York for the 10th Annual Muggers Convention, and attend your opening at this surprisingly first class hotel. May I add, I enjoyed the show very much and could suggest only _one_ thing that would add a touch of richness and depth to your performance."

"I know, I know," a somewhat irritated young Mr. S. said, "your publisher, Michael H. Goldsen, Criterion Music Corp., 6124 Selma Avenue, Hollywood, California, has been at rehearsals every day for the last week trying to get us to include one of your songs in the show."

"A noble thought indeed, for it would surely add more richness and depth to your performance," I spake, cleverly repeating myself.

"Lee, can I tell you something as a friend? Excuse me, an acquaintance."

"Certainly," I said, my sensuous moustache flashing interest.

"Your songs suck! That's right, 'Old Brown Eyes', they s-u-c-k! I have in my short career heard some 'baddies'. And they're all yours!! That they sell is a miracle that dwarfs the creation of life." Said a young Mr. S., again changing his tuxedo and gaining two strokes. "You will someday be punished, yea, punished, for passing yourself off as a songwriter. I make this pledge," he continued, raising his right hand, "that before I sing one of your pygmy melodies in my show, I will first end my career and enter the field of Japanese low-fi repairing. This, I, Frank Sinatra, Jr., being of sound mind and body so solemnly swear. And don't you ever forget it, 'Brown Eyes"!!"

"Oh, I won't," said me, my brown eyes tearing drops of defeat on my seersucker suit.

"See that you don't," he barked, opening the door of his dressing room and walking to the street.

I stood for a minute and cried and wailed and blubbered, until I remembered that greater men than myself had suffered defeat and had never been heard from since. Then, seating myself on a well-worn couch, I sobbed some more. And as I wept, I remembered a story my old Uncle Emory Henry Beenry told me when I was a little shit.

There was once a young taxidermist named Manuel Daniel Samuel, quite successful monetarily, but as yet he walked the world unrecognized by his peers. He had in his short career stuffed a horse for Roy Rogers, stuffed a rhinoceros for John Wayne, stuffed a Republican for President Johnson, and stuffed a gut for Colonel Sanders of fried chicken fame. But alas, Manuel Daniel Samuel was not happy, for he had yet to enjoy critical acclaim. Critics found his stuffing too crass, too plastic, too commercial. His cars and homes and bank accounts gave him little satisfaction. Manuel Daniel Samuel longed for acceptance by the Eastern Critical Clan.

"It never came. It never came. For if it had, the name Manuel Daniel Samuel would have been known and loved throughout the land," my Uncle Emory Henry Beenry often said, "but I'm about the only person who ever heard of him, and I didn't like the sonofabitch!"

This story always cheered me. It didn't stop my crying, but it always cheered me a little. I don't know why . . . just one of life's mysteries, I guess.

"Dopey, do you always look delighted when you're despondent?" asked a beautiful Tina Sinatra, slinking a well-timed entrance.

"Oh, most beautiful Sinatra lady, it has been years since my comatose eyes have fallen on your coruscating loveliness."

"Horse-puckie, Barton. I saw you last week," her lovely mouth spit. "You're falling apart, aren't you, Dopey? Have you been staying out past ten-thirty p.m., sinning and doing the uglies with Hollywood starlets?"

"All you say is true, oh Venus, except the sinning. They won't sin with me. I ask, I beg, I plead, but all I ever get is an occasional peck on the cheek."

"Tough!" her lovely mouth murmured.

"What is wrong with me? _What is wrong with me_? Won't you tell me, dear maiden?"

"Okay," her lovely mouth chimed. "I wouldn't mind going over a few of your faults. Are you ready?"

"I await your constructive criticism as a child longs for Christmas morn'."

"Ach!" she shivered, and began . . ."Number one, your nose looks like a condemned ski shoot. Number two, you dress like a clothes buyer for Mechanics Illustrated. Number three, you're built like a urine specimen bottle. And number four, your teeth have more buck than a rodeo horse. Number five, your talent is the most microscopic I've ever encountered! . . . Had enough?"

"Oh, oh, oh," sniffed me, changing from cheered to teared. "But isn't there something about me you like?"

"Well, let me see," she thought but a second, then asked . . ."You don't sing, do you?"

"Well . . . no . . . but—"

"Good! I like that!" quipped lovely Tina, skipping away on her beautiful legs.

"Hey you," snorted a very thick man, breaking through the door and quickly putting a whole-nelson on I.

"Please sir," I gasped, "pray tell me how can I be of service? If it pleasures you, please inform me with some haste for I feel sure my sudden lack of oxygen brought about by your superior whole-nelson will soon send me swimming in a dark pool of unconscienciousness."

The thick man loosened his grip ever so slightly and bellowed, "The boss wants to see you."

"The boss? Who's the boss?"

"The Man! The Pope! Don't you speak English?" he questioned, easily throwing me across his shoulder and smashing through the remaining dressing room door into the street.

"You mean Pope John would like an audience with me?"

"Not Pope John, 'Brown Eyes", Pope Frank!"

"Oh, oh, OH!" spake me, "_that_ Pope. Right, man, right!" I said trying to sound and look as hip as possible, considering I was still draped quite casually across the thick man's shoulder.

When we reached his car, the thick man quickly unlocked the trunk, tossed me in and drove away. Some fifteen minutes later, we arrived at a Manhattan apartment in the '70's.

"Wait here, 'Brown Eyes'," grunted the thick man, depositing me in a deeply upholstered chair.

Several minutes later the thick man entered the room again with a rather nice looking gentleman.

"Hello," he said. "I'm Nancy's father. We met once before, earlier in the book."

"Yes," I answered, "but just for safety sake, could I – "

"Goddammit!!!!! Here's my Diners Card, my American Express, and my driver's license."

I studied the cards for several minutes and once I had convinced myself this gentleman was really the personage he claimed to be, I assumed my hippest posture and returned the cards saying, "Well, man, like it sure is groovy to lay my peepers on your bones again."

"Let me break his head, boss," the thick man said.

"Not just yet," Nancy's father happily sang. "Tell me, 'Brown Eyes', in thirty words or less, have you ever composed music for films? (And it really pains me to call what you write _music_!)" He said in parenthesis.

"Well, man, it's hard to humble about it, baby, but I have, daddy-o, I mean, like I wrote the score for a Sam Katzman western starring Duane Eddy – "

"Duane? And Eddy?" he interrupted. "I never heard of either of them."

"Well, man," I continued, shifting my weight to my hipper leg, "he was a little after your time. I also wrote the title song for that great AIP color extravaganza, 'The Girl On Death Row'. Surely your peepers focused that one, man!"

"No, no," he pondered, shaking his head. "I don't go to drive-ins much since the kids are grown."

"Oh well, no matter. I just wanted you to know, baby, I'm just explodin' with movie music writing ability. You dig!"

"God, he obnoxious." He whispered to the thick man. "Nancy said he was, but jeeeeezsus, I had no idea!"

"Anyway, 'Harry Hip'," he continued, pointing a stern finger in my left eye, "we're starting a film called 'Tony Rome' in a couple of weeks, and I'd like you to write the title song. (God only knows why!)" he said speaking in parenthesis again. "We'll get in touch with you when we need you."

"Shit, man, I'm gonna lay a little tune on you baby, that'll warp your bird—"

"Take him back where you got him." Mr. S. shouted to the thick man and ran from the room.

THE RETURN OF HA HA HA

THE PHONE RANG.

"Don't answer it," I screamed.

"It's for you," Donnie Owens cried.

"I thought I said don't answer it. Why did you answer the miserable goddamn phone when I said _don't answer it_!"

"You don't know, do you?" Donnie Owens smiled, handing me the dreaded black instrument.

"Hello? Hello, Barton, it's me. I'm home."

"Who is this?"

"It's me. Nancy."

"Nancy who?"

"For godsakes, Barton, I've only been gone for a couple of weeks."

"Oh, welcome home," I enthusiastically chuckled.

"It's not funny, Barton. Viet Nam was rough."

"It wasn't so easy here either, dear heart, but then it never is."

"Well, no matter," she breathed, "I'll bet you really have come up with some great song ideas while I was gone. Huh, Barton??"

Silence.

"Barton? Have you written any new song whilst I've been away?"

"Not a one." I spoke most profoundly.

"Barton?"

"Yes, dear child."

"Get to work, or else!"

"Are you threatening me?" I demanded.

"Yes, I am, Barton!"

"Just checking," I softly whispered, returning the receiver to its home.

"You heard that, Donald! Now let that be a lesson to you. Never answer the phone. It only brings trouble."

"You're right,' Donald grinned. "Here she is now."

Trouble entered the room, walked over and lay across my feet. I couldn't move.

"Pigeon droppings on you, old Great Dane of mine. Arise from my feet, for I must surely go to the bathroom soon as well as perform other duties."

Donald walked over and forced a guitar on me, saying, "Here, since you can't get up, why not write a song or two?"

"What kind of conspiracy is this! You've sold me out, the both of you. I thought you were my friends. Why. . . ? Why are you doing this to me?"

"Nancy has promised Trouble all her Beatle records," snarled Donnie. "I'm just doing it for fun."

"Trouble, you disloyal turd, how could you?"

She barked something that sounded surprisingly like 'you don't know do you!'.

"If you're tired of writing little solo numbers for Nancy 'with the laughing', why don't you write a duet?' Donald suggested.

"It takes two to tango, as well as duet, Donald," retaliated me, "and just who or whom would you suggest for Ha ha ha's singing partner?"

"How about the Pope?"

"He's busy making a movie,"

"How about yourself?"

"But, Donald," I blushingly protested, "I don't sing."

"Your songs are shit too, but that ain't stopped you so far."

"Donald, surely you jest," my blushing crimson lips exclaimed.

"I ain't jested in years, Barton," spoke a slightly leaning James Bowen, entering my sanctuary. He headed straight for the booze cabinet. "Somebody bent my jester," he sang.

"James, I've locked up the Chivas!"

"It's all right, Barton. I brought a crowbar,"

"For christsakes, Donald, open the cabinet," yelled me, tossing him the keys.

"What's the matter, Barton, too cheap to buy house slippers?" mumbled James, pointing to Trouble still sitting on my warm feet.

"Not that it's any of your business, James. But Trouble won't get up."

I thought a moment.

"Maybe she'll listen to you, James. Why don't you make her a nice drink, huh?"

"Not me, 'ole friend. If that hundred and sixty-five pound brown sonofabitch wants to sit on your face, that's her business. I never mix in family affairs," belched James, emptying a half glass of CR and pouring himself another.

"Young James," I warned, "if you get any higher, you can go duck hunting with a rake."

"My, aren't we folksy this evening," slurped James, seating himself in my most comfortable chair. "Barton, to tell the truth, I don't like strong drink. But I must have it. I must have it if I'm to continue listening to the songs you write . . . and I'm here this day to listen."

"I have no new songs, James. None!"

"Good, I'll take an old one.' James said, taking my portfolio from the table. "I need something for Dean Martin. Now, let me see . . . eenie, meenie, miney, mo, catch a Swedish aviator by the goggles, if he hollers ask him for a rate on the 'B' side, o-u-t spells _you_. AH HA!! This one will do just fine."

James roared, tearing the leadsheet from my book and stumbling out the door.

"What did he take?" I questioned Donald.

"(Going Back to) Houston", Donald answered matter of factly.

"It'll never sell! Never sell!! Never!!!" I wept.

"You really _don't_ know, do you, Barton?"

"Houston" single – 1 million+ (worldwide).
"Houston" album – 1 million+ (worldwide).

JEANETTE MCDONALD IN BOOTS – NELSON EDDY IN JEANS

"WHAT HAS THE OKLAHOMA Irving Berlin written for little 'ole Nancy with the laughing face, ha ha ha," asked little 'ole Nancy with the laughing face, ha ha ha .

"I've written a duet."

"Wonderful, 'Oklahoma Irving'. Now if you can find another of me to sing with me, then—"

"No, dear lady. It's a duet for man and woman, boy and girl, plus and minus, positive and negative.'

"Who's going to be my negative?"

"Well, I've considered Bobby Darin."

"Yes?"

"But he records for another label."

"Yes?

"I've considered your father."

"Yes?"

"But he's making a film."

"Yes?"

And I've considered Dean Martin."

"Yes?"

"But he's involved in his weekly television program. So, after much deliberation and considerable soul searching, I've decided to use the most available singer in the world."

"Who's that?"

"Me!"

"Look, 'Oklahoma Irving'!! You're out of your goddamn skull!! You considered Bobby Darin, Dean Martin, my father, and then *yourself*? You've got the most screwed up Mickey Mouse brain, for considering, I've ever seen. Besides, who told you you could sing? Have you ever sang before?"

"No," I proudly blushed, "but it doesn't sound difficult. Donald has been teaching me all he knows, which took almost two hours. And two hillbilly friends of ours, both singers, came by and gave me a few of these little green pills. They said you can't sing good without 'em. I'm probably about as ready as I ever will be," I said rather proudly.

"I wish I were, 'Oklahoma Irving' . . . I wish I were."

THREE WEEKS LATER

"What you're trying to tell me, Barton," Nancy screamed, "is you've conjoined that awful 'Sh-Sh-Sugartown' song, a rather obvious commercial for LSD, with that lustful, degenerate, alcoholic duet,

'Summerwine', and _this_ is my new 45 rpm single recording for Reprise Records, on Warner Boulevard,
Burbank, California, USA?"

"You've got it, tiny little Italian person." I sort of
intellectualized.

"My godfather!! Oh, shame and chicken feath-
ers and a lot of other things, Barton! Have we suc-
cumbed to worldliness? Have we fallen to such lowly
depths of commercialism as to sell badly rhyming
songs praising the virtues of dope, sex and alcohol to
the people of America – nay, the world – on our
small 45 rpm plastic Reprise phonograph records?"

"I must report, Lady Caesar, we have."

"Is it selling?' asked her, quite innocently.

"Oh yes, dear one – looks like a biggie. Probably
a million and a half domestically and –"

"Fantastic! Fantastic!" Nancy 'with the laughing'
said, jumping into the air and slamming her Ferrari
keys quite happily into my skull. "Keep writing, oh,
do keep writing!" exclaimed she, running and dodg-
ing traffic at break-neck speed with clever hopscotch
moves.

LONDON BRIDGE IS FALLING

"HOW'D YOU LIKE TO make a fast trip to London.' A quite excited laughing faced Nancy blasted into my phone receiver. "Hello, Barton! Answer me, dammit! I know you're there. Barton?"

"At the tone, the time will be – "

"Barton! No one with a voice like yours would be giving time signals."

"I'm not giving 'em, I'm selling 'em. Deposit fifteen cents, please."

Look, Barton! I've just signed to sing the title song for 'You Only Live Twice', the new James Bond film. It means lots of money."

"For me?" I questioned.

"Not necessarily, Barton. Not necessarily."

"Well, I don't think I'm interested. Remember, I had to sleep in the manger last time we were there. And I'm very busy writing a song for your dad's new film, and reading what the critics have to say about our first duet, 'Summerwine'. Now that I'm a singing star, I must be very careful about over-exposure. You understand."

"Over-exposure, my asp! You sang with me on the back side of one record and already you're worried about –"

"You can't start worrying too soon in this business."

"Barton, I wouldn't take you to London if you begged me!"

"I know you wouldn't, so I won't. Why don't you take the joyful one with all the cameras? I bet he'd like – Hello? Hello?"

She hung up, thought I. Oh well, no matter. I'll just pour me a big glass of CR and read my reviews.

'Lee Hazlewood, for some unexplainable reason, continues to write and produce trash that sells. Now he has started to sing. Lee's performance on 'Summerwine' is an ardent plea for the legalization of mercy killings. Nancy Sinatra, singing his third rate material, is better than ever.'

"The mating call of an albino elephant who has stewed his left testicle on a barbed wire fence and is being stung to death by Toluca Lake tse-tse flies, is a pleasant sound compared to Lee Hazlewoods' vocalizing on 'Summerwine". Nancy Sinatra is better than ever.'

'Things Congress should investigate:

The spreading menace of vaginal sprays, and Lee Hazlewoods' singing on 'Summerwine'.'

'While dialing across my radio the other evening, I was witness to something that sounded like a cross between a syphilitic grizzly bear gargling Comet Bathroom Bowl Cleanser, and several hundred constipated Malibu mud turtles pleading for Milk of Magnesia. I immediately stopped the car, thinking the end of the world was near. Quickly opening the door, as so many others on the freeway were doing, I dropped to my knees and asked God to forgive my sins. It was then I heard a voice say, 'Fear not. It is only Lee Hazlewood singing on 'Summerwine'.' Nancy Sinatra never sounded better.'

"Donald, have you noticed that critics in general tend to be unsympathetic, biased, miserable farts?' I asked.

"Yes, Barton, I have," mused Donald, "Except in your case, I find them very kind."

WE WENT TO NASHVILLE TO RECORD 'JACKSON' OR WAS IT THE OTHER WAY

"HAVE YOU SEEN IT!! Have you seen it!! Have you seen the marquee out front of the motel!!!" Donald inquired.

"No, 'Ha ha ha' and I came in the back way."

"Well, you finally made it, 'ole buddy," he said, opening the drapes and pointing to the flashing sign reading:

"NANCY AND LEE, WELCOME TO NASH-VILLE"

"That's good, huh, Donnie?"

"That's good? That's the top, my friend! Your name in lights in front of a motel! There's nothing bigger!! Do you know . . . Grampa Jones, Webb Pierce, Faron Young, Chester Atkins, Arly Duff, or Autry Enman would give their left one to see their name in lights in front of a motel like this?" Donald breathlessly proclaimed.

"You know, Donald, I never thought—"

"My god, man!! What more could you want? It's your dream come true. I'm so proud of you I could shit!" Donald screeched, pumping my hand and slapping my back.

I started to seat myself in the closest chair. Nervous success beads burst forth from my forehead. Donald excitedly wet his pants, just as the phone rang.

"Hello."

"Barton, its Nancy."

"Yes, my little Sicilian swallow."

"Don't sit down."

"Why? May I inquire, my Italian incense."

"Because we're moving."

"Moving?"

"You've got it right, buster. I don't like my suite."

"But what about our names on the marquee?"

"Tell 'em to take 'em off!!"

"Take 'em off?" I screamed.

"Tell 'em to take 'em _all_ off!!" she replied.

The fire of fame quickly turned to dung in my soul as I dialed the manager to relate our early departure.

Several hours later in another part of Music City, USA. I heard a knock, knock, knocking at my door.

"Who is it?" I wondered.

"Tis Captain Raven of the Nashville Police. Nothing more," came the Poe-ish reply.

"Yes, Captain?"

"Is this yours?" He asked, shoving a disheveled Donnie Owens through the door.

"Why, yes. Where did you find him?"

"He'd locked himself in the toilet of a motel. He wouldn't come out. That would have been okay, but the fella who'd rented the room thought he also oughta have bathroom privileges. He's a little out of it, so watch the little devil . . . 'green-pilled' I think . . . he keeps mumbling something about 'reaching the top!!' . . . 'this is it' . . . 'hillbilly heaven'. He's a quick little fucker . . . kicked two of Nashville's finest right in the balls before you could say 'Grand Ole Opry' . . . so we had to put the cuffs and leg irons on him."

"That's all right. You're very kind, Captain Raven. If you'll just put him in here." I said, pointing to the closet, "I'm sure he'll be okay in the morning."

'Mr. Hazlewood, we're friendly folks down here in Nashville, and we don't want to press no charges So if you'll just pay these damages, everybody will be willing to forget the whole mess." Captain Raven chirped, handing me an itemized statement.

One outside door to Room 213.	$ 60.00
One bathroom door.	$ 50.00
One sink replacement.	$145.17
One shower curtain.	$ 17.22
One commode lid.	$ 10.48
One commode handle.	$ 4.19
One full length bathroom mirror.	_$ 77.84_
	$364.90

"My god, it's a small fortune!"

"Yes sir, but remember nobody's pressin' charges. Of course, these here are just the things he destroyed while we was tryin' to get to him. If you look on the other side of the paper, you can see what he busted up before we actually got to him."

I quickly turned the paper over.

One 100 foot, 10 in marquee pipe, nickel plated . . .
$1,635.40
One 35 foot x 60 foot marquee. . . . .
_$2,614.10_
$4,249.50

"What he did, I reckon," Captain Raven said, "was try . . . well, he didn't try, he really did . . . saw down the marquee and was trying to pull it away in a stolen taxi when we saw him and he ran in that motel bathroom and locked the door.

"Let me see. Seven plus two is nine and carry the zero . . . my God! My God!!" I said with two exclamation points. "We've been in town less than four hours and one of our asshole entourage has already destroyed $4,614.40 in private property?"

"That's close enough, Mr. Hazlewood," Captain Raven spake ever more.

The phone rang just before my two largest upper teeth nervously stapled my bottom lip to one of my double chins.

"Hello."

"Hello, Barton"

"Look, Nancy—"

"I heard. I heard, Barton. Just tell them to charge it to Reprise records."

"But what will I list it as on the invoice, dear lady." Asked me.

"Toothpaste, snow shoes, Band-Aids, and silver plated back scratchers," came Nancy's snappy reply.

"But what will they say, oh, what will they say." I queried.

"What _can_ they say, What _can_ they," Ha ha ha chuckled.

I thought, 'she's right you know . . . she really is'!

"Goodbye, Italian angel."

"So long, helpless hillbilly,"

The following evenings found us all happily recording cowboy songs, written by the likes of Hank Cochran, Red Blaine, Harland Howard, Billy Ed Wheeler and others. It was Monday, Wednesday, then Friday night, and almost time to go. In fact, we had but twenty minutes left when Ha ha ha suggested she and me record a simple little song titled 'Jackson', which had been recorded earlier by Johnny Cash and June Carter, and I thought it a little repetitive to record it again.

"But," I stammered humbly, when she asked me to sing, "how can I get my voice in shape on such short notice?"

"Barton, get your butt out here and sing! No one will notice, believe me," came her surly reply.

In my excitement, I quietly walked through the glass window surrounding the recording booth. Someone said we would have just enough time to record the song once.

"Do, re, mi, fa—"

"Barton!"

"Sol, la, yes, dear lady."

"Shut up and sing. Sing!"

Everyone agreed one time through was enough. Everyone, that is, except . . ."

"Do, re, mi, fa, sol, la . . ."

"It's too late, Barton," a sober Donnie Owens stated, "the musicians have all gone home."

"Do, re, mi, fa, sol . . ."

"'Ha ha ha' has returned to the ho ho ho hotel."

"Do, re, mi, fa . . ."

"The engineer has turned off the tape machine."

"Do, re, mi . . ."

"And the janitor wants to clean the place."

"Do, re, mi,—my God! I've gone blind!"

"No, Barton. They've just turned out the lights. Follow my 'glow-in-the-dark' guitar," Donnie sang, "and I'll lead you to safety."

"I could have really sang the song better, Donald, I really could have."

"That's what they all say, Barton – Just follow me and –"

"Ouch!" I screamed.

"Watch that beam. It's a little low."

"Thank you, Donald."

"You're welcome, Barton."

MOVIN' WITH
WHAT'S HER "HA"

<u>*MONDAY*</u>:

"Why aren't the stations playing 'You Only Live Twice'? All I ever hear is 'Jackson'. Are you involved in some sort of payola scandal?" Nancy wondered aloud.

"You must not blame me, dear one. I am quite innocent of any chicanery, since I wrote neither of the selections."

"Yes, but I promised the film producer of 'You Only Live Twice' that his song would be a king-size hit."

"Yes, dear one. But, *I* <u>*didn't*</u>!"

"Then we're safe, aren't we, Barton," she smilingly asked.

"Yes, pretty thing, we are. And soon, they tell me you'll have another gold record to add to your growing collection when 'Jackson' sells a million. Does that not please you?"

"Yes, but I have other things on my mind," she yawned. "Look at this," said she, handing me a single sheet of paper.

"What is it?" asked me.

"It's my one-hour TV Special called 'Movin' With Nancy'. What do you think?"

"Well," I said, taking a pencil from my pocket and quickly making a few un-needed changes, "I think it will be just fine . . . just fine."

She suspiciously eyed my additions and turned again to me, smiling.

"Barton, I think we'll make you producer."

"Oh, goody!" sayeth me.

TUESDAY:
"Barton, I've just got some bad news for you," Ha ha ha gulped. "The sponsor and the networks won't accept you as a producer since you've never produced a TV Special. So I've hired Jack Haley, Jr. to produce and direct."

"Is that the one who directs those pornographic ant documentaries?" I asked.

"Yes, it is, and don't be a smart ass, Barton. The network and sponsor like him."

"I like him too, but does he know anything about music?"

"Yes," she replied. "He likes it!"

" . . . well, that's a start."

"Don't worry, Barton. You'll be Writer and Associate Producer."

"Oh, goody, goody," sayeth me.

WEDNESDAY:

"Barton."

"Yes, Italian one."

"We both know you and I wrote this show, right?"

"Right! But it might be more honest, dear one, to say you wrote it but I made some sterling changes with my battery operated lead pencil." came my soft reply.

"Well, the network and sponsor never heard of you. So I had to get someone to write it who's known."

"Like who?"

"Like Tom Mankiewicz."

"Well, he's known all right, but since he's only going to write a few lines for you and Dean Martin, and since the show is nothing but music – does he know anything about music?"

"Yes, Barton. He does!"

"Oh?"

"Yes. He likes it!" came her subtle reply. "Don't worry, Barton, you're still my Associate Producer.'

"What do Associate Producers do?" asked me.

"Very little, Barton, very little."

"Are you sure?" I asked. "Really sure?"

"Yes. Why do you ask?"

"Then don't you think you should make the joyful one with the cameras Associate Producer?"

"You may have something there, Barton – "

"-and Ha ha ha – "

"Yes, Barton?"

"I'll just sing a couple of songs with you and help Billy Strange with the music . . . OK?"

"You're a good man, Barton"

"-and 'you'll some kinda do' for a girl."

THREE WEEKS LATER:
"I surely like the new number you've written for Nancy and yourself to sing. What's it called again?" Jack Haley, Jr. and Tom Mankiewicz asked in unison.
" 'Some Velvet Morning'," came my simple reply. "Well, it's beautiful, beautiful. Would you mind if we called it 'Phaedra'?"
"Yes, I would!"
"Well then, we'll just leave it like it is, won't we? Could you perhaps explain what the lyrics 'some velvet morning when I'm straight I'm going to open up your gate' actually mean? Would you say it's drug-oriented?
"Tsk, Tsk, Tsk. Never, never, never," I replied. "Actually, young Mankiewicz and Haley, Jr., it's a simple story which you should find easy to digest."
"Oh?"
"Yes," I continued, "it's the story of *two* . . . two caught in an underground jungle . . . held by a river of vice and corruption . . . fighting . . . yes, and if need be dying . . . so the world will be a better place for you and me and our children."

Haley, Jr. and Mankiewicz's four eyes teared in unison, and their voices asked, "Pardon our intrusion, but are these *two* – two young people?"
"NO, TWO ANTS!!" I said, patting their famous writer and director backs.
"OUT! OUT! OUT!" they screamed.
-     and I *OUTED*!!
-
SIX WEEKS LATER:

" 'Movin' with Nancy' is a hit. Now I can direct Glen Campbell films. No more fucking ants," said Jack Haley, Jr.

" 'Movin' with Nancy' is a hit. Now I can write James Bond films. No more beach ball movies," said Tom Mankiewicz.

" 'Movin' with Nancy is a hit. Now everyone will want me to score their TV Specials," said Billy Strange.

" 'Movin' with Nancy' is a hit. Now I can stop drinking that . . . boy, a cold Coke would sure taste good right now," said Ha ha ha."

" 'MOVIN' WITH NANCY' IS A HIT. SO I'M MOVIN'", spake 'guess who'.

"But where will you go Barton?" asked the Italian one.

"I think it should be someplace I can spell."

"That's clever. Will you ever return?"

"Yes," I spake, "some day or some night."

"But, Barton," she pleaded, "why are you leaving me at this point in my life and career?"

"So I'll have enough stuff for another book," came my Capitalistic answer.

"That's wise. Very wise. It's been fun, Barton."

"And profitable," said me.

"That too," her replied, "I love you, Barton."

"And I love you, dear heart. Someday I hope we'll play Cowboys and Italians again," twanged me, walking off into the Hollywood sunset and the five o'clock traffic, my Socialistic eyes straining through the smog, hoping to find SAS Airlines.

THE MEEK SHALL INHERIT ADROITNESS

"Well, there he goes. What's you holy opinion, 'Old Larger Than Walmart'?" queried l.i.v.

"I <u>understand</u>eth he has given away all his possessions. His house, his cars, commercial properties and his bank accounts . . . all that he has labored so <u>hard</u>eth and <u>long</u>eth to acquire."

"He didn't exactly <u>give</u> them away, 'Old Taller Than McDonald's', he drew a feminist judge, in a California divorce court and she screwed him without 'nary a kiss. His ex-bride got it all."

"Tis such a sad parable. How <u>will</u>eth he survive?" wondered the BIG SPIRIT.

"Well, 'Old Stronger Than General Motors'. Lee probably keeps more in his boot, than most folks earn in a decade. So, erase the worry lines from your brow. But it's nice you should be concerned . . . however, he stills owns his copyrights and publishing companies, so he should prevail . . . perhaps . . . anyway . . . GOD BLESS HIM!"

"I have . . . and I will!" <u>replied</u>eth the BIG SPIRIT . .

And the Angels sang:
        The hurt I hurt
        Is nothing like
        The hurt I've hurt before
        The things I feel
        Do not feel
        Like the things I've felt before
        And the loneliness
        And the emptiness
        And the hopelessness
        Are fine

        Because sometimes my cloudy brain
        Remembers
        For one moment
        You were mine

        The pain that pains
        Is not the pain
        That's pained my heart before
        The tears I tear
        Are not like the tears
        My eyes have teared before
        And the loneliness
        And the helplessness
        And the uselessness
        Are fine

        Because sometimes my cloudy brain
        Remembers
        For one moment
        You were mine

Song: "For One Moment" – Lee Hazlewood ©

This little mess is dedicated to:
My daughter: Debra Hazlewood-Lesser
My son: Mark Hazlewood
My daughter: Samantha Hazlewood-Stewart

In order of their appearance on earth:
My grandson: Dion Lee Hazlewood
My grandson: Joshua Glenn Lesser
My Granddaughter: Goldie Eva Lee Lesser
My granddaughter: Phaedra Dawn Stewart
My great-grandson: Devyn Angel Hazlewood

And to my love and keeper:
Jeane Kelley-Hazlewood

And let's not forget The Big Spirit (B.S.)
And the little inner voice (l.i.v.)

Til the next time . . .
L.H.